Answers: P.1 — P.5

Section One — Numbers

Types of Number P.1

Q1 4

Q2 -3 °C

Q3 **a)** 6 ÷ 2 = 3, rational
b) $\sqrt{16}$ = 4, rational
c) $\sqrt{5}$ = 2.23606..., irrational
d) 3 ÷ 8 = 0.375, rational
e) $\sqrt[3]{25}$ = 2.92401..., irrational
f) Rational

Q4 **a)** the third cube number (27)
b) the fourth square number (16)

Q5 **a)** 2
b) e.g. 29
c) 19
d) 19 and 2
e) e.g. 1 or 25

Q6 **a)**

1	(2)	(3)	4	(5)	6	(7)	8	9	10
(11)	12	(13)	14	15	16	(17)	18	(19)	20
21	22	(23)	24	25	26	27	28	(29)	30
(31)	32	33	34	35	36	(37)	38	39	40
(41)	42	(43)	44	45	46	(47)	48	49	50
51	52	(53)	54	55	56	57	58	(59)	60
(61)	62	63	64	65	66	(67)	68	69	70
(71)	72	(73)	74	75	76	77	78	(79)	80
81	82	(83)	84	85	86	87	88	(89)	90
91	92	93	94	95	96	(97)	98	99	100

b) 3 of: 11 (11), 13 (31), 17 (71), 37 (73), 79 (97)
c) e.g. 3 is a factor of 27

Q7 113

Q8 There's just one: 2 is the only even prime.

Multiples, Factors and Prime Factors P.2-P.3

Q1 **a)** 12
b) 3
c) 1, 9
d) 1, 3, 9
e) P = 12, Q = 6

Q2 Any 5 of:
2 groups of 24, 3 groups of 16,
4 groups of 12, 6 groups of 8,
8 groups of 6, 12 groups of 4,
16 groups of 3, 24 groups of 2.

Q3 The Conversational French and Woodturning classes both have a prime number of pupils and so cannot be divided into equal groups.

Q4 **a)** 1, 8, 27, 64, 125
b) 8, 64
c) 27
d) 8, 64
e) 125

Q5 **a)** 2×3^2
b) $2^2 \times 5 \times 7$
c) 47

Q6 **a)** 2, 3, 5, 7, 11
b) 28
c) $2^2 \times 7$

Q7 **a)** 1, 3, 5, 7, 9
b) 25
c) 5^2

Q8 **a)** 495
b) $3 \times 5 \times 11$

Q9 **a)** 1, 4, 9, 16, 25, 36, 49, 64, 81, 100
b) 4, 16, 36, 64, 100
c) 9, 36, 81
d) 1, 64
e) Total = 385 = $5 \times 7 \times 11$

Q10 **a)** $50 \times 25 \times 16 = 20{,}000$ cm^3
b) $2^5 \times 5^4$
c) 200. It is not enough to divide the large volume by the smaller volume as the shapes of the blocks are important too. It is possible to fit 16 ÷ 4 = 4 small blocks across the width, 50 ÷ 5 = 10 small blocks along the length and 25 ÷ 5 = 5 small blocks down the height of the large block. This enables Gordon to fit 4 × 10 × 5 = 200 small blocks into the big block

Q11 **a)** 680
b) $2^2 \times 5 \times 17$
c) $2 \times 5 \times 17$
d) 5×17

Q12 42

LCM and HCF P.4

Q1 **a)** 6, 12, 18, 24, 30, 36, 42, 48, 54, 60
b) 5, 10, 15, 20, 25, 30, 35, 40, 45, 50
c) 30

Q2 **a)** 1, 2, 3, 5, 6, 10, 15, 30
b) 1, 2, 3, 4, 6, 8, 12, 16, 24, 48
c) 6

Q3 **a)** 20
b) 10
c) 2
d) 15
e) 15
f) 5
g) 32
h) 16
i) 16

Q4 **a)** 120
b) 120
c) 120
d) 45
e) 90
f) 180
g) 64
h) 192
i) 192

Q5 **a)** 7th June
b) 16th June
c) Sunday (1st July)
d) Lars

Fractions P.5-P.7

Q1 **a)** $\frac{1}{64}$
b) $\frac{1}{9}$
c) $\frac{1}{18}$
d) $3\frac{29}{32}$
e) $5\frac{5}{32}$
f) $\frac{81}{100\,000}$

Q2 **a)** 1
b) 4
c) $\frac{1}{2}$
d) $\frac{2}{5}$
e) $\frac{10}{33}$
f) 1000

Q3 **a)** $\frac{1}{4}$
b) $\frac{5}{6}$
c) $\frac{1}{2}$
d) $4\frac{3}{8}$
e) $5\frac{3}{8}$
f) 1

Q4 $3\frac{7}{15}$, so the bowl will be big enough.

Q5 **a)** 0
b) $\frac{1}{2}$
c) $-\frac{1}{6}$
d) $1\frac{7}{8}$
e) $-3\frac{1}{8}$
f) $\frac{4}{5}$

Q6 **a)** $\frac{3}{4}$
b) $\frac{5}{12}$
c) $\frac{7}{15}$
d) $4\frac{3}{4}$
e) 4
f) $1\frac{1}{5}$
g) $\frac{5}{8}$
h) $-\frac{1}{24}$
i) $4\frac{3}{5}$
j) $1\frac{1}{30}$

Answers: P.5 — P.14

k) 1
l) $\frac{44}{75}$

Q7 a) 1/12
b) 1/4
c) 2/3

Q8 a) 3/4 of the programme
b) 5/8 of the programme
c) 1/8 of the programme

Q9 3/5 of the kitchen staff are girls.
2/5 of the employees are boys.

Q10 7/30 of those asked had no opinion.

Q11 a) 12/30 = 2/5
b) 6 days

Q12 a) Each box will hold 16 sandwiches. So 5 boxes will be needed for 80 sandwiches.
b) 25 inches tall

Q13 a) $\frac{1}{18}$
b) $\frac{1}{4}$

Q14 a) 48 km^2
b) $\frac{5}{8}$

Q15 a) 8 people
b) $\frac{7}{20}$
c) $\frac{1}{4}$
d) 57 people
e) 65 people

Q16 After the 1st bounce the ball reaches 4 m, after the 2nd $2\frac{2}{3}$ m, after the 3rd $1\frac{7}{9}$ m.

Q17 a) 100 g flour
b) 350 g
c) $\frac{2}{7}$
d) 300 g

Q18 £31.06

Fractions, Decimals and Percentages P.8-P.9

Q1 a) 25%
b) 50%
c) 75%
d) 10%
e) 41.52%
f) 84.06%
g) 39.62%
h) 28.28%

Q2 a) 0.5
b) 0.12
c) 0.4
d) 0.34
e) 0.602
f) 0.549
g) 0.431
h) 0.788

Q3 a) 50%
b) 25%
c) 12.5%
d) 75%
e) 4%
f) 66.7%
g) 26.7%
h) 28.6%

Q4 a) 1/4
b) 3/5
c) 9/20
d) 3/10
e) 41/500
f) 62/125
g) 443/500
h) 81/250

Q5 85%

Q6 Grade C

Q7 a) 0.3 e) 1.75
b) 0.37 f) 0.125
c) 0.4 g) 0.6
d) 0.375 h) 0.05

Q8

Fraction	Decimal
1/2	0.5
1/5	0.2
1/8	0.125
8/5	1.6
4/16	0.25
7/2	3.5
x/10	0.x
x/100	0.0x
3/20	0.15
9/20	0.45

Q9 a) $0.8\dot{3}$ e) $0.\overline{90}$
b) $0.\dot{7}$ f) $0.\overline{460317}$
c) $0.\overline{63}$ g) $0.\overline{478}$
d) $0.\overline{47}$ h) $0.\overline{5891}$

Q10 a) $\frac{3}{5}$ e) $\frac{1}{3}$
b) $\frac{3}{4}$ f) $\frac{2}{3}$
c) $\frac{19}{20}$ g) $\frac{1}{9}$
d) $\frac{16}{125}$ h) $\frac{16}{99}$

Q11 a) $\frac{2}{9}$ e) $\frac{4}{33}$
b) $\frac{4}{9}$ f) $\frac{545}{999}$
c) $\frac{8}{9}$ g) $\frac{251}{333}$
d) $\frac{80}{99}$ h) $\frac{52}{333}$

Percentages P.10-P.12

Q1 a) £1.28
b) 629 kg
c) 16 mins

Q2 a) 0.2 c) 0.02
b) 0.35 d) 0.625

Q3 a) $\frac{1}{5}$ c) $\frac{7}{10}$
b) $\frac{3}{100}$ d) $\frac{421}{500}$

Q4 a) 12.5% c) 30%
b) 23% d) 34%

Q5 85%

Q6 72.5%

Q7 a) £4275 b) £6840

Q8 1.6%

Q9 500%

Q10 £358.80

Q11 £244.40

Q12 23 028

Q13 Car 1 costs £8495 – (0.15 × £8495) = £8495 – £1274.25 = £7220.75.
Car 2 costs £8195 – (0.12 × £8195) = £8195 – £983.40 = £7211.60.
So car 2 is the cheapest.

Q14 £5980

Q15 £152.75, So NO, he couldn't afford it.

Q16 31%

Q17 13%

Q18 a) 67.7%
b) 93.5%
c) 38.1%

Q19 38%

Q20 £80

Q21 a) 300
b) 4 whole years

Q22 a) £236.25
b) £1000 × 1.07^3 – £1000 = £225.04
c) £1000 × 1.07875^3 – £1000 = £255.34

Compound Growth and Decay P.13-P.14

Q1 a) £473.47 c) £909.12
b) £612.52 d) £1081.90

Q2 a) 280
b) 3035
c) 27 hours

Q3 a) 8.214 kg c) 7.272 kg
b) 7.497 kg d) 3.836 kg

Q4 a) £1920.80 c) £434.06
b) £27 671.04 d) £34 974.86

Q5 Second option by £2.20

Q6 £462.08

Q7 £3162.91

Q8 a) 910.91
b) 754.32
c) 114.39
d) about 30 hours

Q9 a) £7877.94 d) £10 646.54
b) £27 116.06 e) £7184.25
c) £9980.90 f) £5843.70

Answers: P.14 — P.21

Q10 **a)** £128 606
b) £103 788
c) £77 974
d) £475 000

Q11 **a)** 51
b) 52
c) 50
d) 61

Q12 **a)** 16.85 million
b) 20.72 million

Ratios P.15-P.16

Q1 **a)** 3:4 **b)** 1:4 **c)** 1:2 **d)** 9:16 **e)** 7:2 **f)** 9:1

Q2 **a)** 6 cm **b)** 11 cm **c)** 30.4 m **d)** 1.5 cm **e)** 2.75 cm **f)** 7.6 m

Q3 **a)** £8, £12
b) 80 m, 70 m
c) 100 g, 200 g, 200 g.
d) 1hr 20 m, 2 hr 40 m, 4 hrs.

Q4 John 4, Peter 12

Q5 400 ml, 600 ml, 1000 ml

Q6 30

Q7 Jane £40, Holly £48, Rosemary £12

Q8 Paul — £16

Q9 **a)** 250/500 = 1/2
b) 150/500 = 3/10

Q10 **a)** 245 girls
b) 210 boys

Q11 **a)** 39
b) 140

Q12 **a)** 1:300
b) 6 m
c) 3.3 cm

Q13 **a)** 15 kg
b) 30 kg
c) 8 kg cement, 24 kg sand and 48 kg gravel.

Q14 **a)** 30 fine
b) 15 not fine
c) 30/45 = 2/3

Q15 **a)** 45 Salt & Vinegar
b) 90 bags sold altogether

Rounding Numbers P.17-P.18

Q1 **a)** 62.2
b) 62.19
c) 62.194
d) 19.62433
e) 6.300
f) 3.142

Q2 **a)** 1330
b) 1330
c) 1329.6
d) 100
e) 0.02
f) 0.02469

Q3 **a)** 457.0
b) 456.99
c) 456.987
d) 457
e) 460
f) 500

Q4 2.83

Q5 **a)** 0.704 (to 3 s.f. — the least number of significant figures used in the question).
b) 3.25 (to 3 s.f. — the least number of significant figures used in the question).

Q6 **a)** £1100 **b)** £88 **c)** £300 **d)** £3 **e)** £376 **f)** £44

Q7 23 kg

Q8 £5.07

Q9 235 miles

Q10 £19

Q11 £4.77

Q12 235 cm

Q13 470 cm

Q14 1810 g

Q15 13 s

Estimating P.19

Q1 Mark's tank is approximately 4500 cm^3, so it won't be big enough.

Q2 **a)** $6500 \times 2 = 13\ 000$
b) $8000 \times 1.5 = 12\ 000$
c) $40 \times 1.5 \times 5 = 300$
d) $45 \div 9 = 5$
e) $35\ 000 \div 7000 = 5$
f) $\frac{55 \times 20}{10} = 55 \times 2 = 110$
g) $7000 \times 2 = 14\ 000$
h) $100 \times 2.5 \times 2 = 500$
i) $20 \times 20 \times 20 = 8000$
j) $8000 \div 80 = 100$
k) $62\ 000 \div 1000 = 62$
l) $3 \div 3 = 1$

Q3 Approximately 15 000 – (1500 + 2500 + 1500 + 1500 + 3000) = 5000

Q4 **a)** $\frac{150 + 50}{150 - 50} = \frac{200}{100} = 2$
b) $\frac{20 \times 10}{\sqrt{400}} = \frac{200}{20} = 10$
c) $\frac{2000 \times 4}{20 \times 5} = \frac{8000}{100} = 80$
d) $\frac{10^2 \div 10}{4 \times 5} = \frac{10}{20} = 0.5$

Q5 **a)** $2 \times (3 \times 3) + 2 \times (2 \times 3.5) = 36\ m^2$
b) 3 tins

Q6 **a)** 6.9 (accept 6.8)
b) 10.9 (accept 10.8)
c) 9.2 (accept 9.1)
d) 4.1 (accept 4.2)
e) 9.9 (accept 9.8)
f) 5.8 (accept 5.9)

Bounds P.20-P.21

Q1 **a)** 64.785 kg
b) 64.775 kg

Q2 **a)** 1.75 m
b) $1.85 \times 0.75 = 1.3875\ m^2$

Q3 **a)** 2.525 l
b) 2.475 l

Q4 **a)** 95 g
b) Upper bound = 97.5 g, lower bound = 92.5 g.
c) No, since the lower bound for the electronic scales is 97.5 g, which is greater than the upper bound for the scales in part **a)**.

Q5 **a)** Upper bound = 13.5, lower bound = 12.5
b) Upper bound = 12.55, lower bound = 12.45
c) To calculate the upper bound for C multiply the upper bound for A by the upper bound for B;
$13.5 \times 12.55 = 169.425$
To calculate the lower bound for C multiply the lower bound for A by the lower bound for B;
$12.5 \times 12.45 = 155.625$

Q6 **a)** Upper bound = 5 minutes 32.5 seconds, lower bound = 5 minutes 27.5 seconds.
b) The lower bound for Jimmy's time is 5 minutes 25 seconds, which is lower than the lower bound for Douglas' time (5 minutes 25.5 seconds).

Q7 **a)** Upper bound = 945, lower bound = 935.
b) Upper bound = 5.565, lower bound = 5.555.
c) To find the upper bound for R, divide the upper bound for S by the lower bound for T;
$945 \div 5.555 = 170.117...$
To find the lower bound for R, divide the lower bound for S by the upper bound for T;
$935 \div 5.565 = 168.014...$
d) $940 \div 5.56 = 170$ (to 2 s.f. — the upper and lower bounds both round to 170 to 2 s.f., but give different answers to 3 s.f.).

Q8 At least 18.2 m^2

Answers: P.21 — P.25

Q9 The upper bound for the distance is 127.5 km. The lower bound for the time is 1 hour and 45 minutes = 1.75 hours. The maximum value of the average speed is 127.5÷1.75 = 72.857... km/hour.

Q10 a) Perimeter = 2(12 + 4) = 32 cm. Maximum possible error = 4 × 0.1 cm = 0.4 cm.
b) Maximum possible error in P is $2(x + y)$.

Standard Form P.22-P.23

Q1 **a)** 35.6 **b)** 3560 **c)** 0.356 **d)** 35600 **e)** 8.2 **f)** 0.00082 **g)** 0.82 **h)** 0.0082 **i)** 1570 **j)** 0.157 **k)** 157000 **l)** 15.7

Q2 **a)** 2.56×10^0 **b)** 2.56×10 **c)** 2.56×10^{-1} **d)** 2.56×10^4 **e)** 9.52×10 **f)** 9.52×10^{-2} **g)** 9.52×10^4 **h)** 9.52×10^{-4} **i)** 4.2×10^3 **j)** 4.2×10^{-3} **k)** 4.2×10 **l)** 4.2×10^2

Q3 **a)** 3.47×10^2 **b)** 7.3004×10 **c)** 5×10^0 **d)** 9.183×10^5 **e)** 1.5×10^7 **f)** 9.371×10^6 **g)** 7.5×10^{-5} **h)** 5×10^{-4} **i)** 5.34×10^0 **j)** 6.2103×10^2 **k)** 1.49×10^4 **l)** 3×10^{-7}

Q4 6×10^{-3}

Q5 1×10^9, 1×10^{12}

Q6 9.46×10^{12}

Q7 6.9138×10^4

Q8 1.2×10^{-2} (mm)

Q9 **a)** Mercury
b) Jupiter
c) Mercury
d) Neptune
e) Venus and Mercury
f) Jupiter, Neptune and Saturn

Q10 **a)** 6×10^9 **b)** 1.89×10^7 **c)** 4×10^4 **d)** 2×10^2 **e)** 5.6×10^{16} **f)** 3.99×10^4 **g)** 4.3473×10^6 **h)** 1.748×10^4

Q11 **a)** 2.4×10^{10}
b) 1.6×10^6
c) 1.8×10^5

Q12 1.04×10^{13} is greater by 5.78×10^{12}

Q13 1.3×10^{-9} is smaller by 3.07×10^{-8}

Q14 **a)** 4.2×10^7
b) 3.8×10^{-4}
c) 1.0×10^7
d) 1.12×10^{-4}
e) 8.43×10^5
f) 4.232×10^{-3}
g) 1.7×10^{18}
h) 2.83×10^{-4}
i) 1×10^{-2}

Q15 7×10^6

Q16 6.38×10^8 cm

Q17 3.322×10^{-27} kg

Q18 **a)** 1.8922×10^{16} m
b) 4.7305×10^{15} m

Q19 **a)** 510000000 km^2
b) 3.62×10^8 km^2
c) 148000000 km^2

Section Two — Algebra

Sequences P.24

Q1 **a)** 10, 12, 14; even numbers
b) 9, 11, 13; odd numbers
c) 25, 36, 49; square numbers
d) 125, 216, 343; cube numbers

Q2 **a)** 31, 36, 41
b) 5
c) 5n + 1
d) 101

Q3 **a)** 2n
b) 2n – 1
c) 5n
d) 3n + 2

Q4 **a)** 19, 22, 25, $3n + 4$
b) 32, 37, 42, $5n + 7$
c) 46, 56, 66, $10n – 4$
d) 82, 89, 96, $7n + 47$

Q5 No.

Q6 **a)** 4n – 3
b) 75 is not in the sequence because when the expression is set to equal 75, n is not a whole number.

Q7 24, 35, 48

Q8 **a)** $16\frac{7}{8}$, $16\frac{9}{16}$, $16\frac{23}{32}$, $16\frac{41}{64}$
b) The 10th term will be the mean of the 8th and 9th terms.

Powers and Roots P.25-P.26

Q1 **a)** 16
b) 1000
c) 3 × 3 × 3 × 3 × 3 = 243
d) 4 × 4 × 4 × 4 × 4 × 4 = 4096
e) 1 × 1 × 1 × 1 × 1 × 1 × 1 × 1 × 1=1
f) 5 × 5 × 5 × 5 × 5 × 5 = 15 625

Q2 **a)** 2^8 (or 256)
b) 12^5 (or 248 832)
c) x^5
d) m^3
e) y^4
f) z^6

Q3 **b)** 10^7
c) 10^6
d) 10^8
e) Simply add the powers.

Q4 **b)** 2^3
c) 4^2
d) 8^3
e) Simply subtract the powers.

Q5 **a)** true **b)** true **c)** false **d)** false **e)** true **f)** false **g)** false **h)** true **i)** false **j)** true **k)** true **l)** false

Answers: P.25 — P.30

Q6 a) 3^{-3} d) 3^{-12}
b) 4^{25} e) 4^{6}
c) 10^{-13} f) 5^{3}

Q7 a) 275 b) 0.123
c) 53 400 d) 6.40×10^{-5}
e) 2.37 f) 2.31
g) 10.4 h) 0.843
i) 2.25 j) 2.18
k) 0.244 l) 0.965

Q8 a) 8.76 b) 4.17
c) 19.4 d) 219
e) 108 f) 91.9
g) 13.6 h) 17.8
i) 5.06

Q9 a) 0.008 b) 0.25
c) 1.53×10^{-5} d) 0.667
e) 2.24 f) 1.82
g) 1.55 h) 2.60
i) 0.512 j) 1.21
k) 0.0352 l) 7.28

Q10 a) 1.49 b) 20.1
c) 2.50 d) 6.55
e) 1.08 f) 8.78
g) 0.707 h) –0.380

Q11 a) 9.14 b) 1.50
c) 0.406 d) 476
e) 0.0146 f) 1.22
g) 84.5 h) 0.496
i) 165 j) 8.47

Algebra Basics P.27

Q1 a) -27°C d) +18°C
b) -22°C e) +15°C
c) +12°C f) -12°C

Q2 Expression **b)** is larger by 1.

Q3 a) $-4x$ b) $18y$

Q4 a) –1000, –10 c) 144, 16
b) –96, –6 d) 0, 0

Q5 -4

Q6 a) $-6xy$ g) $\frac{-5x}{y}$
b) $-16ab$ h) 3
c) $8x^2$ i) –4
d) $-16p^2$ j) –10
e) $\frac{10x}{y}$ k) $4x$
f) $\frac{-10x}{y}$ l) $-8y$

Q7 a) $15x^2 - x$
b) $13x^2 - 5x$
c) $-7x^2 + 12x + 12$
d) $30abc + 12ab + 4b$
e) $18pq + 8p$
f) $17ab - 17a + b$
g) $4pq - 5p - 9q$
h) $16x^2 - 4y^2$
i) $abc + 10ab - 11cd$
j) $-2x^2 + y^2 - z^2 + 6xy$

Q8 a) $x^2 + 4x + 3x + 12 = x^2 + 7x + 12$
b) $4x^2 + 6x + 6x + 9 = 4x^2 + 12x + 9$
c) $15x^2 + 3x + 10x + 2$
$= 15x^2 + 13x + 2$

Multiplying Out Brackets P.28

Q1 a) $4x + 4y - 4z$
b) $x^2 + 5x$
c) $-3x + 6$
d) $9a + 9b$
e) $-a + 4b$
f) $2x - 6$
g) $4e^2 - 2f^2 + 10ef$
h) $16m - 8n$
i) $6x^2 + 2x$
j) $-2ab + 11$
k) $-2x^2 - xz - 2yz$
l) $3x - 6y - 5$
m) $-3a - 4b$
n) $14pqr + 8pq + 35qr$
o) $x^3 + x^2$
p) $4x^3 + 8x^2 + 4x$
q) $8a^2b + 24ab + 8ab^2$
r) $7p^2q + 7pq^2 - 7q$
s) $16x - 8y$

Q2 a) $x^2 - 2x - 3$
b) $x^2 + 2x - 15$
c) $x^2 + 13x + 30$
d) $x^2 - 7x + 10$
e) $x^2 - 5x - 14$
f) $28 - 11x + x^2$
g) $6x - 2 + 9x^2 - 3x = 9x^2 + 3x - 2$
h) $6x^2 - 12x + 4x - 8 = 6x^2 - 8x - 8$
i) $4x^2 + x - 12x - 3 = 4x^2 - 11x - 3$
j) $4x^2 - 8xy + 2xy - 4y^2$
$= 4x^2 - 4y^2 - 6xy$
k) $12x^2 - 8xy + 24xy - 16y^2$
$= 12x^2 - 16y^2 + 16xy$
l) $9x^2 + 4y^2 + 12xy$

Q3 $15x^2 + 10x - 6x - 4 = 15x^2 + 4x - 4$

Q4 $4x^2 - 4x + 1$

Q5 a) $(4x + 6)$ m
b) $(-3x^2 + 17x - 10)$ m²

Q6 a) $(8x + 20)$ cm
b) $40x$ cm²
c) $40x - 12x = 28x$ cm²

Q7 a) Perimeter — $3x + 29$ cm
Area — $\frac{7x + 126}{2}$ cm²
b) Perimeter — $(8x + 4)$ cm
Area — $(3x^2 + 14x - 24)$ cm²
c) Perimeter — $(16x - 4)$ cm
Area — $(16x^2 - 8x + 1)$ cm²
d) Perimeter — $(10x + 4)$ cm
Area — $(6x^2 - 5x - 6)$ cm²

Factorising P.29

Q1 a) $a^2(b + c)$
b) $a^2(5 + 13b)$
c) $a^2(2b + 3c)$
d) $a^2(a + y)$
e) $a^2(2x + 3y + 4z)$
f) $a^2(b^2 + ac^2)$

Q2 a) $x(x - 5)$
b) $2(x + 3)$
c) $3x(x + 4)$
d) $2x(2x - 3)$
e) $3xy(1 + 4x)$
f) $3(3x + 5)$
g) $5x(3xy - 5)$
h) $4pq(q - 5 + 2p)$
i) $2x(5x^3 + 3)$
j) $5x^2(3x - 4)$
k) $7x(3x + 2)$
l) $5xy(z + 4u)$

Q3 a) $4xyz(1 + 2) = 12xyz$
b) $4xyz(2 + 3) = 20xyz$
c) $8xyz(1 + 2x)$
d) $4xyz^2(5xy + 4)$

Q4 a) $(x + 3)(x - 3)$
b) $(y + 4)(y - 4)$
c) $(5 + z)(5 - z)$
d) $(6 + a)(6 - a)$
e) $(2x + 3)(2x - 3)$
f) $(3y + 2)(3y - 2)$
g) $(5 + 4z)(5 - 4z)$
h) $(1 + 6a)(1 - 6a)$
i) $(x^2 + 6)(x^2 - 6)$
j) $(x^2 + y^2)(x^2 - y^2)$
k) $(1 + ab)(1 - ab)$
l) $(10x + 12y)(10x - 12y)$

Q5 a) $(x + 2)(x - 2)$
b) $(12 + y^2)(12 - y^2)$
c) $(1 + 3xy)(1 - 3xy)$
d) $(7x^2y^2 + 1)(7x^2y^2 - 1)$

Q6 a) $16a^2b^2(4b - a)$
b) $q(p + r - pqr)$
c) $3(m^2 - 8)$
d) $b^2(b^2 - ab + c)$
e) $(a^2 - 13)(a^2 + 13)$
f) $3ab(3b - c)$
g) $(9 - z)(9 + z)$
h) $(6m - 5n)(6m + 5n)$
i) $mn(m + 3 - 2n^2)$
j) $(11p - 3q)(11p + 3q)$
k) $12(12x^2 - 9y^2 - 5z^2)$
l) $(8ab - 7cd)(8ab + 7cd)$

Manipulating Surds P.30

Q1 a) $\sqrt{15}$
b) 2
c) x
d) x
e) 8
f) $\sqrt{5}$

Answers: P.30 — P.35

Q2 3π cm^2

Q3 a) 1 b) $5\sqrt{3}$ c) $2\sqrt{2}$ d) $7 + 4\sqrt{3}$ e) $3\sqrt{5}$ f) $5\sqrt{2}$ g) $\sqrt{2}$ h) $3(\sqrt{2} - 1)$

Q4 a) $(1 + \sqrt{5})(1 - \sqrt{5}) = -4$, rational
b) $\frac{1+\sqrt{5}}{1-\sqrt{5}} = -\frac{1}{2}(3 + \sqrt{5})$, irrational

Q5 a) $(x + y)(x - y) = -1$, rational
b) $\frac{x+y}{x-y} = -3 - 2\sqrt{2}$, irrational

Q6 a) $\frac{\sqrt{2}}{2}$ b) $\frac{\sqrt{2}}{2}$ c) $\frac{\sqrt{10a}}{10}$ d) $\frac{\sqrt{xy}}{y}$ e) $\sqrt{2} - 1$ f) $3 - \sqrt{3}$ g) $\frac{2[\sqrt{6} - 1]}{5}$ h) $\frac{3+\sqrt{5}}{2}$

Solving Equations P.31-P.32

Q1 1

Q2 a) $x = \pm 3$ b) $x = \pm 6$ c) $x = \pm 3$ d) $x = \pm 3$ e) $x = \pm 1$

Q3 a) $x = 5$ b) $x = 4$ c) $x = 10$ d) $x = -6$ e) $x = 5$ f) $x = 9$

Q4 a) $x = 5$ b) $x = 2$ c) $x = 8$ d) $x = 17$ e) $x = 6$ f) $x = 5$ g) $x = \pm 2$

Q5 a) 15.5 cm b) 37.2 cm

Q6 £15.50

Q7 a) $x = 9$ b) $x = 2$ c) $x = 3$ d) $x = 3$ e) $x = 4$ f) $x = -1$ g) $x = 15$ h) $x = 110$ i) $x = \pm 6$ j) $x = 66$ k) $x = 700$ l) $x = 7\frac{1}{2}$

Q8 a) Joan — £x
Kate — £$2x$
Linda — £$(x - 232)$
b) $4x = 2632$
$x = 658$
c) Kate — £1316
Linda — £426

Q9 a) $2x + 32$ cm
b) $12x$ cm^2
c) $x = 3.2$

Q10 a) $x = 0.75$ b) $x = -1$ c) $x = -6$ d) $x = -1$ e) $x = 4$ f) $x = 13$

Q11 $x = 8$

Q12 $x = 1$

Q13 8 yrs

Q14 39, 35, 8

Q15 a) $y = 22$ b) $x = 8$ c) $z = -5$ d) $x = 19$ e) $x = 23$ f) $x = 7$ g) $x = \pm 3$ h) $x = \pm 4$ i) $x = \pm 7$

Q16 $x = 1\frac{1}{2}$

Q17 a) $x = 5$ b) $x = 9$

Q18 $x = 1\frac{1}{2}$ AB = 5 cm
AC = $5\frac{1}{2}$ cm
BC = $7\frac{1}{2}$ cm

Rearranging Formulas P.33-P.34

Q1 a) $h = \frac{10 - g}{4}$
b) $c = 2d - 4$
c) $k = 3 + \frac{j}{2}$
d) $b = \frac{3a}{2}$
e) $g = \frac{8f}{3}$
f) $x = 2(y + 3)$
g) $t = 6(s - 10)$
h) $q = \pm\frac{\sqrt{p}}{2}$

Q2 a) $c = \frac{w - 500m}{50}$
b) 132

Q3 a) i) £38.00 ii) £48.00
b) $c = 28 + 0.25n$
c) $n = 4(c - 28)$
d) i) 24 miles ii) 88 miles
iii) 114 miles

Q4 a) $x = \pm\sqrt{y + 2}$
b) $x = y^2 - 3$
c) $s = \pm 2\sqrt{r}$
d) $g = 3f - 10$
e) $z = 5 - 2w$
f) $x = \pm\sqrt{\frac{3v}{h}}$
g) $a = \frac{v^2 - u^2}{2s}$
h) $u = \pm\sqrt{v^2 - 2as}$
i) $g = \frac{4\pi^2 l}{t^2}$

Q5 a) £Jx
b) $P = T - Jx$
c) $J = \frac{T - P}{x}$
d) £16

Q6 a) i) £2.04 ii) £3.48
b) C = $(12x + 60)$ pence
c) $x = \frac{C - 60}{12}$
d) i) 36 ii) 48 iii) 96

Q7 a) $x = \frac{z}{y + 2}$
b) $x = \frac{b}{a - 3}$
c) $x = \frac{y}{4 - z}$
d) $x = \frac{3z + y}{y + 5}$
e) $x = \frac{-2}{y - z}$ or $\frac{2}{z - y}$
f) $x = \frac{2y + 3z}{2 - z}$
g) $x = \frac{-y - wz}{yz - 1}$ or $\frac{y + wz}{1 - yz}$
h) $x = \frac{-z}{4}$

Q8 a) $p = \frac{4r - 2q}{q - 3}$
b) $g = \frac{5 - 2e}{f + 2}$
c) $b = \frac{3c + 2a}{a - c}$
d) $q = \pm\sqrt{\frac{4}{p - r}} = \pm\frac{2}{\sqrt{p - r}}$
e) $a = \frac{2c + 4b}{4 + c - d}$
f) $x = \pm\sqrt{\frac{-3y}{2}}$
g) $k = \pm\sqrt{\frac{14}{h - 1}}$
h) $x = \left(\frac{4 - y}{2 - z}\right)^2$
i) $a = \frac{b^2}{3 + b}$
j) $m = -7n$
k) $e = \frac{d}{50}$
l) $y = \frac{x}{3x + 2}$

Q9 a) $y = \frac{x}{x - 1}$
b) $y = \frac{-3 - 2x}{x - 1}$ or $\frac{2x + 3}{1 - x}$
c) $y = \pm\sqrt{\frac{x + 1}{2x - 1}}$
d) $y = \pm\sqrt{\frac{1 + 2x}{3x - 2}}$

Factorising Quadratics P.35

Q1 a) $(x + 5)(x - 2)$
$x = -5, x = 2$
b) $(x - 3)(x - 2)$
$x = 3, x = 2$
c) $(x - 1)^2$
$x = 1$
d) $(x - 3)(x - 1)$
$x = 3, x = 1$
e) $(x - 5)(x + 4)$
$x = 5, x = -4$
f) $(x + 1)(2x - 5)$
$x = -1, x = \frac{5}{2}$
g) $(3x + 7)(x - 1)$
$x = -\frac{7}{3}, x = 1$
h) $(x + 7)^2$
$x = -7$
i) $(x - 5)(2x + 3)$
$x = 5, x = -\frac{3}{2}$

Answers: P.35 — P.40

Q2 **a)** $(x + 8)(x - 2)$
$x = -8, x = 2$
b) $(x + 9)(x - 4)$
$x = -9, x = 4$
c) $(x + 9)(x - 5)$
$x = -9, x = 5$
d) $x(x - 5)$
$x = 0, x = 5$
e) $x(x - 11)$
$x = 0, x = 11$
f) $(x - 7)(x + 3)$
$x = 7, x = -3$
g) $(x - 30)(x + 10)$
$x = 30, x = -10$
h) $(x - 24)(x - 2)$
$x = 24, x = 2$
i) $(x - 9)(x - 4)$
$x = 9, x = 4$
j) $(x + 7)(x - 2)$
$x = -7, x = 2$
k) $(x + 7)(x - 3)$
$x = -7, x = 3$
l) $(x - 5)(x + 2)$
$x = 5, x = -2$
m) $(x - 6)(x + 3)$
$x = 6, x = -3$
n) $(x - 9)(x + 7)$
$x = 9, x = -7$
o) $(x + 4)(x - 3)$
$x = -4, x = 3$

Q3 $x = \frac{1}{2}, x = -\frac{1}{2}$

Q4 $x = 4$

Q5 **a)** $(x^2 - x)$ m^2
b) $x = 3$

Q6 **a)** $x(x + 1)$ cm^2
b) $x = 3$

Q7 **a)** x^2 m^2
b) $12x$ m^2
c) $x^2 + 12x - 64 = 0$
$x = 4$

The Quadratic Formula P.36-P.37

Q1 **a)** 1.87, 0.13
b) 2.39, 0.28
c) 1.60, - 3.60
d) 1.16, -3.16
e) 0.53, -4.53
f) -11.92, -15.08
g) -2.05, -4.62
h) 0.84, 0.03

Q2 **a)** -2, -6
b) 0.67, -0.5
c) 3, -2
d) 2, 1
e) 3, 0.75
f) 3, 0
g) 0.67
h) 0, -2.67
i) 4, -0.5
j) 4, -5
k) 1, -3
l) 5, -1.33
m) 1.5, -1
n) -2.5, 1
o) 0.5, 0.33
p) 1, -3
q) 2, -6
r) 2, -4

Q3 **a)** 0.30, -3.30
b) 3.65, -1.65
c) 0.62, -1.62
d) -0.55, -5.45
e) -0.44, -4.56
f) 1.62, -0.62
g) 0.67, -4.00
h) -0.59, -3.41
i) 7.12, -1.12
j) 13.16, 0.84
k) 1.19, -4.19
l) 1.61, 0.53
m) 0.44, -3.44
n) 2.78, 0.72

Q4 **a)** 1.7, -4.7
b) -0.27, -3.73
c) 1.88, -0.88
d) 0.12, -4.12
e) 4.83, -0.83
f) 1.62, -0.62
g) 1.12, -1.79
h) -0.21, -4.79
i) 2.69, -0.19
j) 2.78, 0.72
k) 1, 0
l) 1.5, 0.50

Q5 $x^2 - 3.6x + 3.24 = 0$
$x = 1.8$

Q6 **a)** $x^2 + 2.5x - 144.29 = 0$
$x = 10.83$
b) 48.3 cm

Completing the Square P.38

Q1 **a)** $(x - 2)^2 - 9$
b) $(x - 1)^2$
c) $(x + \frac{1}{2})^2 + \frac{3}{4}$
d) $(x - 3)^2$
e) $(x - 3)^2 - 2$
f) $(x - 2)^2 - 4$
g) $(x + 1\frac{1}{2})^2 - 6\frac{1}{4}$
h) $(x - \frac{1}{2})^2 - 3\frac{1}{4}$
i) $(x - 5)^2$
j) $(x - 5)^2 - 25$
k) $(x + 4)^2 + 1$
l) $(x - 6)^2 - 1$

Q2 **a)** $x = 0.30, x = -3.30$
b) $x = 2.30, x = -1.30$
c) $x = 0.65, x = -4.65$
d) $x = 0.62, x = -1.62$
e) $x = 4.19, x = -1.19$
f) $x = 2.82, x = 0.18$
g) $x = 1.46, x = -0.46$
h) $x = 2.15, x = -0.15$

Algebra Crossword

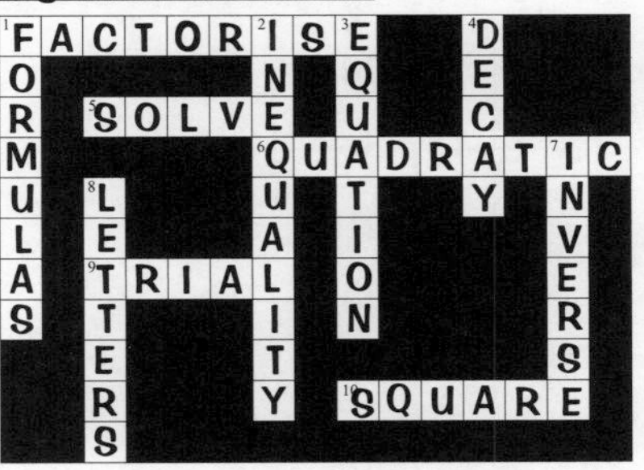

Algebraic Fractions P.39-P.40

Q1 **a)** $\frac{3xy}{z}$
b) $\frac{12b^2}{c}$
c) $\frac{1}{3xy^2z^3}$
d) $\frac{q^3}{2r^3}$

Q2 **a)** $\frac{2}{xy}$
b) $\frac{3a^2b}{2}$
c) $\frac{y}{2x^2}$
d) $\frac{2qr^2}{3}$
e) $\frac{8x^2z^2}{y}$
f) $\frac{90ac^4}{b}$
g) $\frac{x^3}{5}$
h) $\frac{12a^3b^2}{5}$
i) $\frac{3a^4c^3}{2bd}$
j) 1
k) $\frac{3rt^2}{2}$
l) $\frac{d^6}{e^3f}$

Q3 **a)** $2x^2y$
b) a
c) $\frac{3x^2}{y}$
d) $\frac{pq}{2}$
e) $2ef$
f) $5x^3$
g) $\frac{12yz}{x}$
h) $\frac{4a^3}{b}$
i) $\frac{5a^3}{b}$
j) $\frac{2x}{y^2z}$
k) $\frac{6}{n}$
l) $\frac{7g}{f}$

Q4 **a)** $\frac{3a - 4}{2}$
b) $\frac{2x - y}{4}$
c) $\frac{5x + 6}{3}$

Q5 **a)** $x = 5$
b) $x = 2$

Q6 **a)** $\frac{3 + y}{2x}$
b) $\frac{1 + y}{x}$
c) $\frac{2xy}{z}$
d) $\frac{6x + 1}{3}$
e) $\frac{7x + 6}{x}$
f) $\frac{14x + y}{6}$
g) $\frac{3x + 2 + y}{24}$
h) $\frac{x + 2y - 2}{10}$
i) $\frac{7x}{6}$
j) $\frac{37x}{42}$
k) $\frac{x(y + 3)}{3y}$
l) $\frac{xyz + 4x + 4z}{4y}$

Answers: P.40 — P.44

Q7 a) $\frac{4x-5y}{3}$ b) $\frac{4x-1}{y}$ c) $\frac{4x+3y-2}{2x}$ d) $\frac{2-2x}{x}$ e) $\frac{-1}{4x}$ f) $\frac{4x-y}{6}$ g) $\frac{z}{15}$ h) $\frac{m(12-n)}{3n}$ i) $\frac{b(14-a)}{7a}$ j) $\frac{-p+5q}{10}$ k) $\frac{-3p-4q}{4}$ l) $\frac{9x-4y+xy}{3y}$

Q8 a) $\frac{a^2}{b^2}$ b) 1 c) $\frac{3}{2r}$ d) $\frac{mn(pm+1)}{p^2}$ e) $\frac{2x}{x^2-y^2}$ f) $\frac{11}{6x}$ g) $\frac{2(a^2+b^2)}{a^2-b^2}$ h) $\frac{3}{4}$ i) $\frac{3x-6y}{8}$

Inequalities P.41-P.42

Q1 a) $9 \le x < 13$
b) $-4 \le x < 1$
c) $x \ge -4$
d) $x < 5$
e) $x > 25$
f) $-1 < x \le 3$
g) $0 < x \le 5$
h) $x < -2$

Q2

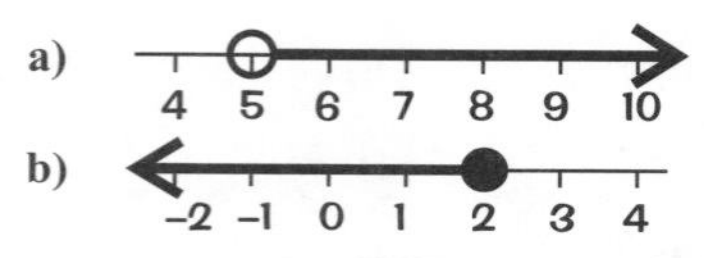

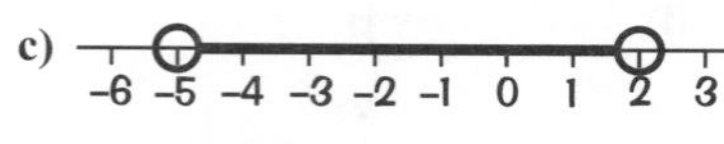

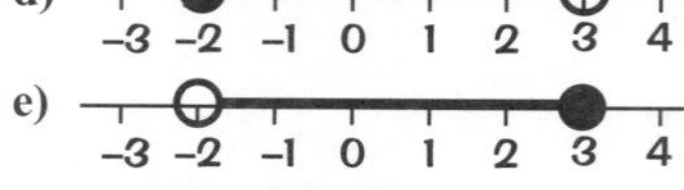

g) –4 –3 –2 –1 0 1 2

h) –4 –3 –2 –1 0 1 2

Q3 a) $x > 3$
b) $x < 4$
c) $x \le 5$
d) $x \le 6$
e) $x \ge 7.5$
f) $x < 4$
g) $x < 7$
h) $x < 4$
i) $x \ge 3$
j) $x > 11$
k) $x < 3$

l) $x \ge -½$
m) $x \le -2$
n) $x > 5$
o) $x < 15$
p) $x \ge -2$

Q4 Largest integer for x is 2.

Q5 $\frac{11-x}{2} < 5$, $x > 1$

Q6 $1130 \le 32x$
36 classrooms are needed.

Q7 50 guests (including bride and groom), $900 \ge 18x$

Q8 $x \ge 2$, $y > 1$, $x + y \le 5$

Q9

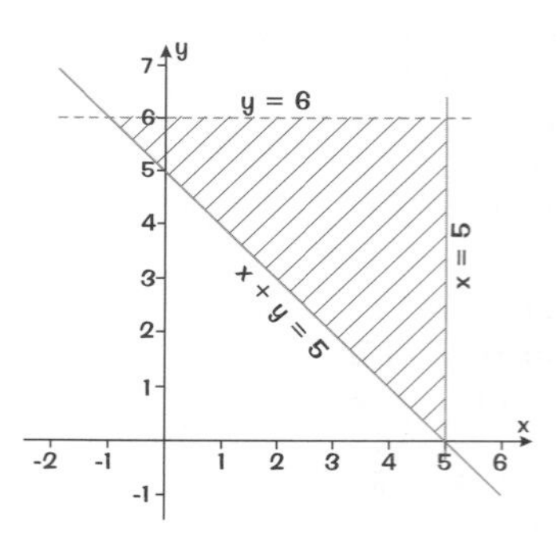

Q10

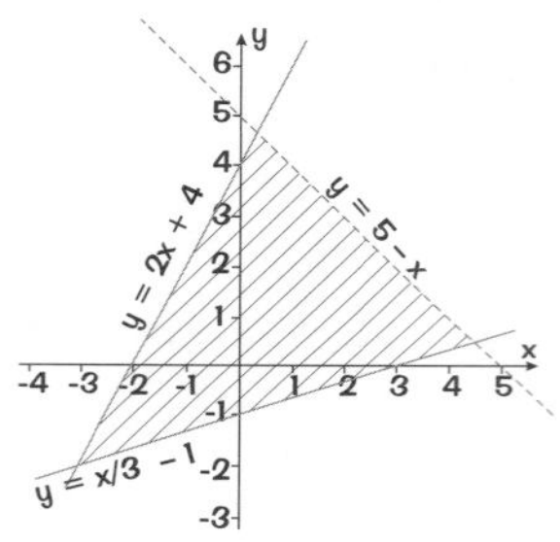

Q11 a) $x > 5$, $y \ge 7$, $x + y \ge 14$
b)

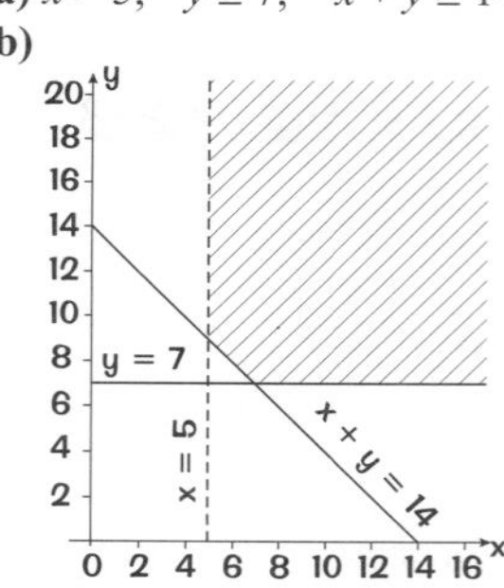

Trial and Improvement P.43

Q1

Guess (x)	value of $x^3 + x$	Too large/ small
2	$2^3 + 2 = 10$	Too small
3	$3^3 + 3 = 30$	Too large
2.6	$(2.6)^3 + 2.6 = 20.2$	Too small
2.7	$(2.7)^3 + 2.7 = 22.4$	Too small
2.8	$(2.8)^3 + 2.8 = 24.8$	Too large
2.75	$(2.75)^3 + 2.75 = 23.5$	Too small

So to 1 d.p. the solution is $x = 2.8$

Q2

Guess (x)	value of $x^3 + x^2 - 4x$	Too large/ small
-3	$(-3)^3 + (-3)^2 - 4(-3) = -6$	Too small
-2	$(-2)^3 + (-2)^2 - 4(-2) = 4$	Too large
-2.1	$(-2.1)^3 + (-2.1)^2 - 4(-2.1) = 3.549$	Too large
-2.2	$(-2.2)^3 + (-2.2)^2 - 4(-2.2) = 2.99$	Too small
-2.15	$(-2.15)^3 + (-2.15)^2 - 4(-2.15) = 3.3$	Too large

So to 1 d.p. the solution is $x = -2.2$

Guess (x)	value of $x^3 + x^2 - 4x$	Too large/ small
-1	$-1 + 1 + 4 = 4$	Too large
0	$0 + 0 - 0 = 0$	Too small
-0.8	$(-0.8)^3 + (-0.8)^2 - 4(-0.8) = 3.328$	Too large
-0.7	$(-0.7)^3 + (-0.7)^2 - 4(-0.7) = 2.947$	Too small
-0.75	$(-0.75)^3 + (-0.75)^2 - 4(-0.75) = 3.141$	Too large

So to 1 d.p. the solution is $x = -0.7$

Guess (x)	value of $x^3 + x^2 - 4x$	Too large/ small
1	$1 + 1 - 4 = -2$	Too small
2	$8 + 4 - 8 = 4$	Too large
1.9	$(1.9)^3 + (1.9)^2 - 4(1.9) = 2.869$	Too small
1.95	$(1.95)^3 + (1.95)^2 - 4(1.95) = 3.417$	Too large

So to 1 d.p. the solution is $x = 1.9$

Q3 Try different values of x to 1 d.p. between 3 and 4 to see which gives the highest value of V, e.g:

Guess (x)	value of $4x^3 - 80x^2 + 400x$
3	108 – 720 + 1200 = 588
4	256 – 1280 + 1600 = 576
3.5	171.5 – 980 + 1400 = 591.5
3.4	157.216 – 924.8 + 1360 = 592.416
3.3	143.748 – 871.2 + 1320 = 592.548
3.2	131.072 – 819.2 + 1280 = 591.872

So to 1 d.p. the solution is $x = 3.3$

Simultaneous Equations and Graphs P.44

Q1 a) $x = 3, y = 3$
b) $x = 2, y = 5$
c) $x = 1, y = 2$
d) $x = 1, y = 2$
e) $x = 1, y = 4$
f) $x = 1, y = 2$
g) $x = 2, y = 3$
h) $x = 2, y = 3$
i) $x = 5, y = 2$
j) $x = 3, y = 4$

Q2 a) $x = 0, x = 1$
b) $x = 2.7, x = -0.7$
c) $x = 3.4, x = -2.4$
d) $x = 1.6, x = -2.6$
e) $x = 0.7$
f) $x = 3.4, x = -2.4$
g) $x = 1.6, x = -2.6$

Answers: P.44 — P.47

Q3

x	-4	-3	-2	-1	0	1	2	3	4
$-\frac{1}{2}x^2$	-8	-4.5	-2	-0.5	0	-0.5	-2	-4.5	-8
+5	5	5	5	5	5	5	5	5	5
y	-3	0.5	3	4.5	5	4.5	3	0.5	-3

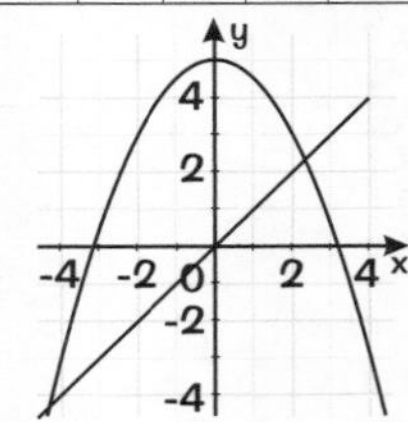

a) $x = 3.2, x = -3.2$
b) $x = 4, x = -4$
c) $x = 2.3, x = -4.3$

Simultaneous Equations P.45

Q1 **a)** $x = 4, y = 18$ OR $x = -3, y = 11$
b) $x = 6, y = 28$ OR $x = -3, y = 1$
c) $x = 1.5, y = 4.5$ OR $x = -1, y = 2$
d) $x = -3, y = 33/5$ OR $x = 2, y = \frac{28}{5}$
e) $x = -\frac{1}{4}, y = \frac{17}{4}$ OR $x = -3, y = 40$
f) $x = -\frac{2}{3}, y = \frac{31}{3}$ OR $x = -4, y = 57$

Q2 **a)** $x = 1, y = 2$
b) $x = 0, y = 3$
c) $x = -1\frac{1}{2}, y = 4$
d) $x = 5, y = 23$ OR $x = -2, y = 2$
e) $x = \frac{1}{3}, y = -\frac{29}{3}$ OR $x = 4, y = 38$
f) $x = \frac{1}{2}, y = -\frac{3}{2}$ OR $x = -2, y = 6$
g) $x = 1, y = 9$
h) $x = 8, y = -\frac{1}{2}$
i) $x = -1, y = 3$

Q3 **a)** $6x + 5y = 430$
$4x + 10y = 500$
b) $x = 45, y = 32$

Q4 7 chickens
4 cats

Q5 5 g (jellies are 4 g)

Q6 $3y + 2x = 18$
$y + 3x = 6$ $\quad x = 0, y = 6$

$4y + 5x = 7$
$2x - 3y = 12$ $\quad x = 3, y = -2$

$4x - 6y = 13$
$x + y = 2$ $\quad x = 2\frac{1}{2}, y = -\frac{1}{2}$

Q7 $5m + 2c = 344$
$4m + 3c = 397$ $\quad m = 34\text{p}, c = 87\text{p}$

Q8 $x = 12, y = 2$

Direct and Inverse Proportion P.46

Q1 $y = 20$

Q2 $y = 184.8$

Q3 $y = 2$

Q4 $x = 2$

Q5

x	1	2	3	4	5	6
y	48	24	16	12	9.6	8

Q6

x	1	2	5	10
y	100	25	4	1

x	2	4	6	8
y	24	6	$2\frac{2}{3}$	1.5

Q7 4 kg

Q8 **a)** $r = 96$
b) $s = 4$
c) $r = 600$
d) $s = -8$

Q9 9.5 N kg^{-1}

Proof P.47

Q1 $(n + 3)^2 - (3n + 5)$
$= (n + 3)(n + 3) - (3n + 5)$
$= n^2 + 6n + 9 - 3n - 5$
$= n^2 + 3n + 2 + 2$
$= (n + 1)(n + 2) + 2$

Q2 $(n - 3)^2 - (n - 5)$
$= (n - 3)(n - 3) - (n - 5)$
$= n^2 - 6n + 9 - n + 5$
$= n^2 - 7n + 12 + 2$
$= (n - 3)(n - 4) + 2$

Q3 $25 - \frac{(x-8)^2}{4}$
$= \frac{100 - (x-8)^2}{4}$
$= \frac{-x^2 + 16x + 36}{4}$
$= \frac{(2+x)(18-x)}{4}$

Q4 $(2n + 1)^2 - (2n - 1)^2 - 10$
$= (4n^2 + 4n + 1) - (4n^2 - 4n + 1) - 10$
$= 8n - 10$
Dividing this by 8 gives $n - \frac{5}{4}$ (not a whole number), so the total is not divisible by 8.

Q5 $n + (n + 1) + (n + 2)$
$= 3n + 3 = 3(n + 1)$
Dividing this by 3 gives $n + 1$ (a whole number), so the total is divisible by 3.

Q6 $2a \times 2b = 4ab$, which must be even.

Q7 $2n + (2n + 2) + (2n + 4)$
$= 6n + 6 = 6(n + 1)$
Dividing this by 6 gives $n + 1$ (a whole number), so the total is a multiple of 6.

Q8 **a)** $(2n + 1) + (2n + 3)$
$= 4n + 4 = 4(n + 1)$
Dividing this by 4 gives $n + 1$ (a whole number), so the total is a multiple of 4.
b) $(2n + 1)^2 + (2n + 3)^2$
$= 4n^2 + 4n + 1 + 4n^2 + 12n + 9$
$= 8n^2 + 16n + 10$
Dividing this by 4 gives
$= 2n^2 + 4n + \frac{5}{2}$ (not a whole number), so the total is not divisible by 4.

Q9 2 is a prime number as it only divides by 1 and itself. 2 is even so Maisy is wrong.

Q10 **a)** 3 and 1 are both odd numbers but if you add them together you get 4, which is even so the statement is wrong.
b) If $n = 6$, $n^2 = 36$ so the statement is wrong as 36 is divisible by 4 but 6 is not divisible by 4.

Q11 If $a = 1$ and $b = -1$, then $a^2 = 1$ and $b^2 = 1$. So, $a^2 = b^2$, but a does not equal b, so the statement is wrong.

Answers: P.48 — P.53

Section Three — Graphs

X, Y and Z Coordinates P.48-P.49

Q1

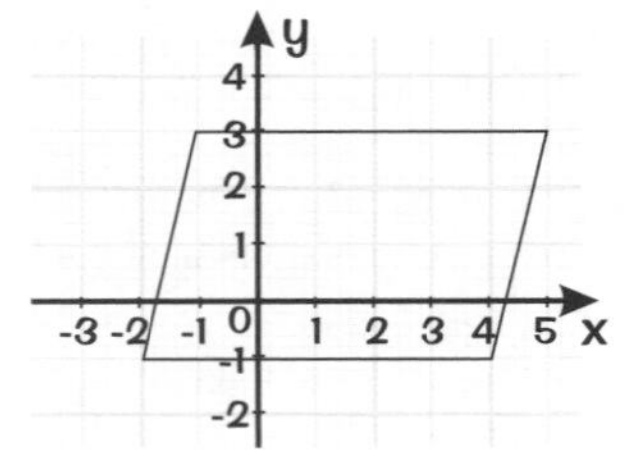

missing coordinate = (5,3)

Q2

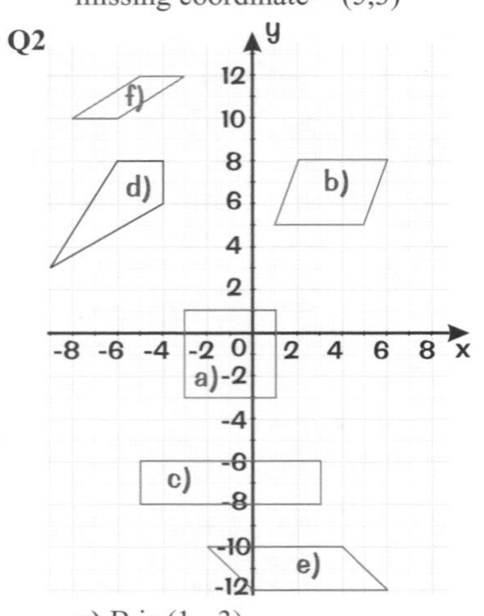

a) B is (1, -3)
b) C is (5, 5)
c) A is (-5, -8)
d) D is (-4, 6)
e) D is (0, -12)
f) C is (-3, 12)

Q3

C = (2, 1), D = (2, -2)

Q4 **a)** (3,4)
b) (5.5,5)
c) (5.5,11)
d) (8.5,9)
e) (3,3.5)
f) (9.5,9.5)
g) (20,41.5)
h) (30.5,20.5)

Q5 (110, 135)

Q6 **a)** (2,5.5)
b) (0.5,1.5)
c) (2,–2.5)
d) (1,–1)
e) (2,3)
f) (4,–0.5)
g) (–13,–12.5)
h) (–5,–7)

Q7 B (1, 5, 8), C (4, 5, 8), D (4, 2, 8)
E (4, 2, 3), F (1, 2, 3), G (1, 5, 3)

Straight-Line Graphs P.50-P.51

Q1 **a)** B **b)** A **c)** F **d)** G **e)** E **f)** F **g)** C **h)** B **i)** D **j)** H

Q2

x	-4	-3	-2	-1	0	1	2	3	4
3x	-12	-9	-6	-3	0	3	6	9	12
-1	-1	-1	-1	-1	-1	-1	-1	-1	-1
y	-13	-10	-7	-4	-1	2	5	8	11

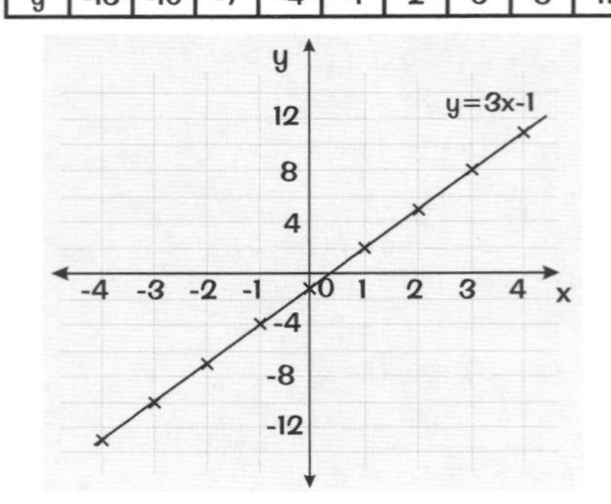

Q3

x	-6	-4	-2	0	2	4	6
1/2 x	-3	-2	-1	0	1	2	3
-3	-3	-3	-3	-3	-3	-3	-3
y	-6	-5	-4	-3	-2	-1	0

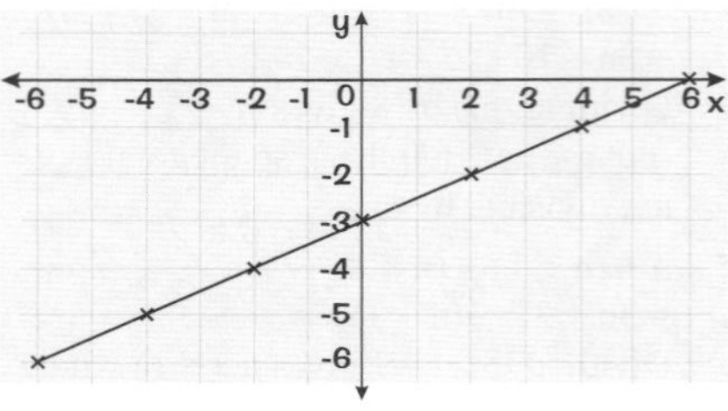

Q4

x	0	3	8
y	3	9	19

a) 13 **b)** 7 **c)** 4 **d)** 7

Q5

x	-8	-4	8
y	-5	-4	-1

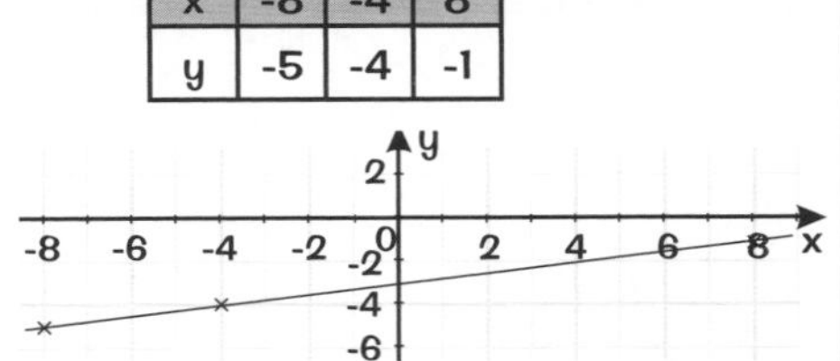

a) -2.5 **b)** -3 **c)** 4 **d)** 6

Q6

Number of Units used	0	100	200	300
Cost using method A	10	35	60	85
Cost using method B	40	45	50	55

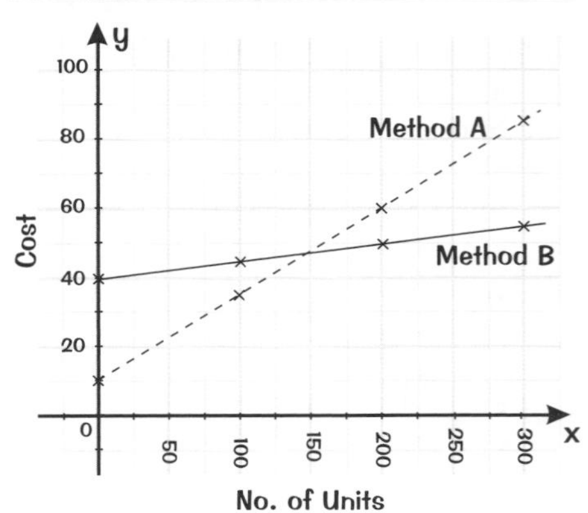

a) i) £27.50 **ii)** £43.50
b) Method A
c) 150 units

Finding the Gradient P.52

Q1 **a)** $-\frac{1}{2}$
b) 3
c) $-\frac{1}{4}$
d) -2
e) $-\frac{2}{3}$
f) $-\frac{8}{3}$
g) 4
h) 1
i) -1
j) $\frac{1}{3}$
k) $-\frac{1}{2}$
l) 3
m) 4

Q2 **a)** 2
b) $\frac{1}{2}$
c) -1
d) -2
e) $\frac{1}{2}$
f) $-\frac{3}{4}$

Q3 **a)** A and C.
b) B: $y = 3x - 1$
So gradient of D = $\frac{-1}{3}$

Q4 The gradient is -0.23 so it's a red run.

"y = mx + c" P.53

Q1 **a)** $m = 4$, (0, 3)
b) $m = 3$, (0, -2)
c) $m = 2$, (0, 1)
d) $m = -3$, (0, 3)

Answers: P.53 — P.58

e) $m = 5$, (0, 0)
f) $m = -2$, (0, 3)
g) $m = -6$, (0, -4)
h) $m = 1$, (0, 0)
i) $m = -\frac{1}{2}$, (0, 3)
j) $m = \frac{1}{4}$, (0, 2)
k) $m = \frac{4}{3}$, (0, 2)

Q2 **a)** $y = \frac{7}{2}x - 1$ **d)** $y = \frac{1}{4}x - 3$
b) $y = \frac{1}{2}x + 4$ **e)** $y = -\frac{1}{2}x$
c) $y = -\frac{1}{5}x + 7$ **f)** $y = -2x - 6$

Q3 **a)** $y = x + 4$ **c)** $y = -x$
b) $y = 3x + 2$ **d)** $y = -3x + 4$

Q4 **a)** $y = x$ **c)** $y = -3x + 3$
b) $y = 3x$ **d)** $y = -2x - 4$

Q5 **a)** $x = 4$ **c)** $y = 7$
b) $x = 8$ **d)** $y = 9$

Q6 (7, 20) and (5, 14)

Quadratic Graphs P.54

Q1

x	-4	-3	-2	-1	0	1	2	3	4
$y=2x^2$	32	18	8	2	0	2	8	18	32

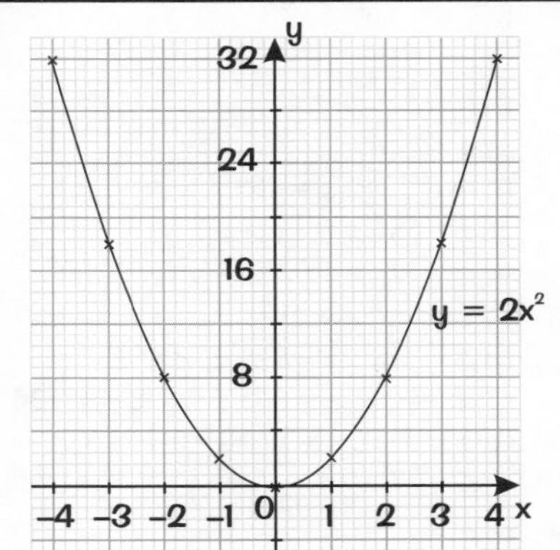

Q2

x	-4	-3	-2	-1	0	1	2	3	4
x^2	16	9	4	1	0	1	4	9	16
$y=x^2+x$	12	6	2	0	0	2	6	12	20

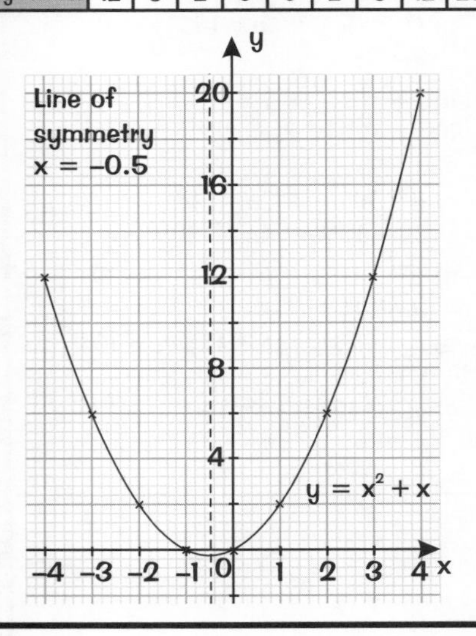

Q3 **a)**

x	-4	-3	-2	-1	0	1	2	3	4
3	3	3	3	3	3	3	3	3	3
$-x^2$	-16	-9	-4	-1	0	-1	-4	-9	-16
$y=3-x^2$	-13	-6	-1	2	3	2	-1	-6	-13

b)

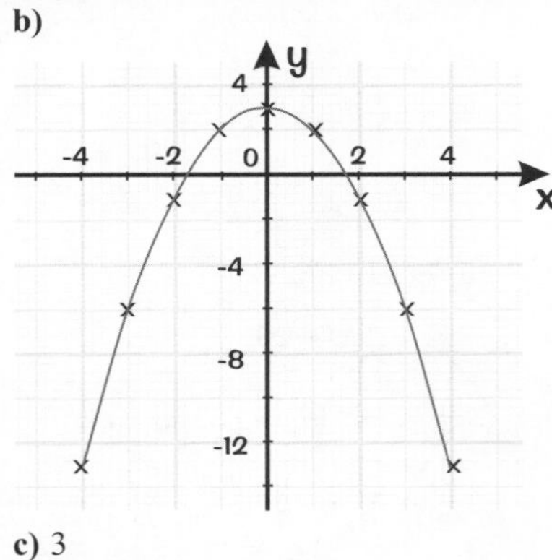

c) 3

Harder Graphs P.55-P.58

Q1 **a)** Cubic
b) Straight Line
c) Reciprocal
d) Quadratic
e) Cubic
f) Reciprocal
g) Exponential
h) Quadratic
i) Straight Line
j) Cubic
k) Cubic
l) Quadratic

Q2 **a) — vii)** **i) — vi)**
b) — i) **j) — xii)**
c) — x) **k) — iv)**
d) — viii) **l) — xiii)**
e) — v) **m) — iii)**
f) — xiv) **n) — ii)**
g) — xi) **o) — ix)**
h) — xv)

Q3

x	-3	-2	-1	0	1	2	3
x^3	-27	-8	-1	0	1	8	27
+4	4	4	4	4	4	4	4
y	-23	-4	3	4	5	12	31

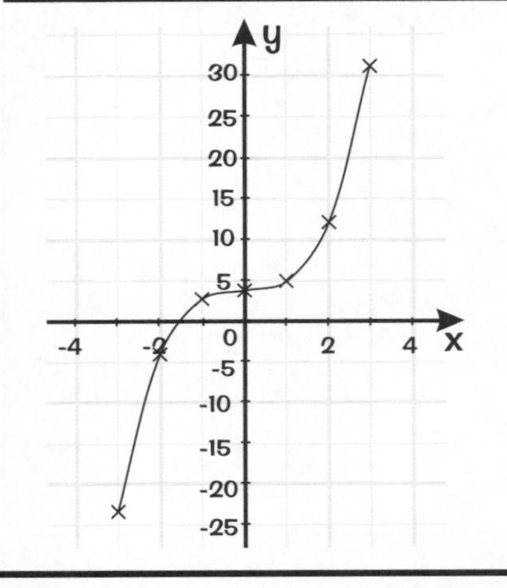

Q4

x	-3	-2	-1	0	1	2	3
$-x^3$	27	8	1	0	-1	-8	-27
-4	-4	-4	-4	-4	-4	-4	-4
y	23	4	-3	-4	-5	-12	-31

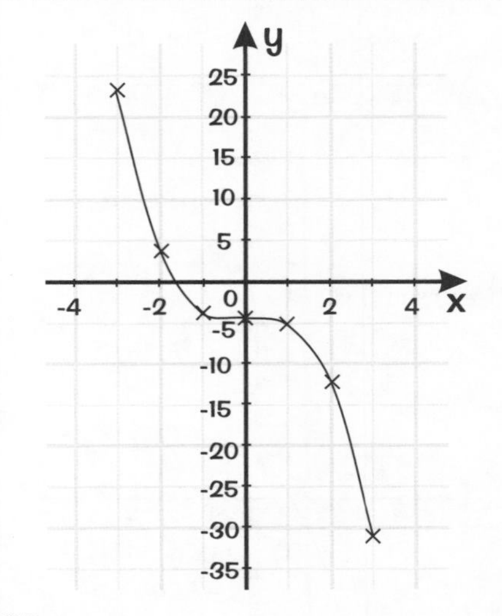

Q5

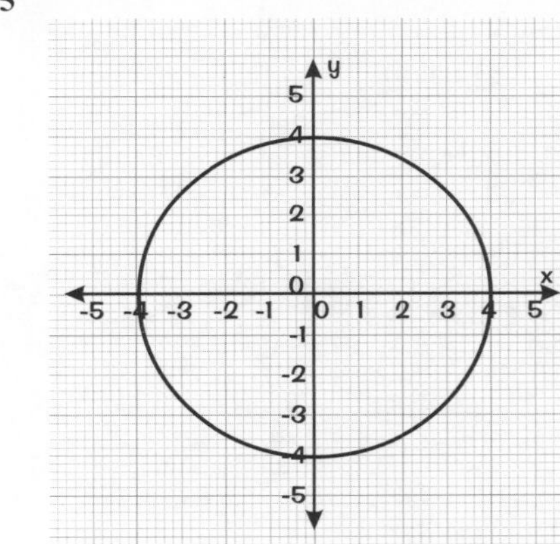

Q6 A(180,0)
B(90,1) C(–90,–1)

Q7 D(270,0) F(0,1)
E(90,0) G(–90,0)

Q8 A $y = \sin(x)$
B $y = \cos(x)$
C $y = \cos(x)$
D $y = \sin(x)$
E $y = \sin(x)$
F $y = \sin(x)$
G $y = \cos(x)$
H $y = \sin(x)$
I $y = \cos(x)$

Q9

x	0	90	180	270	360
y	2	1	0	1	2

Answers: P.59 — P.63

Graph Transformations P.59-P.60

Q1 a) to **d)**

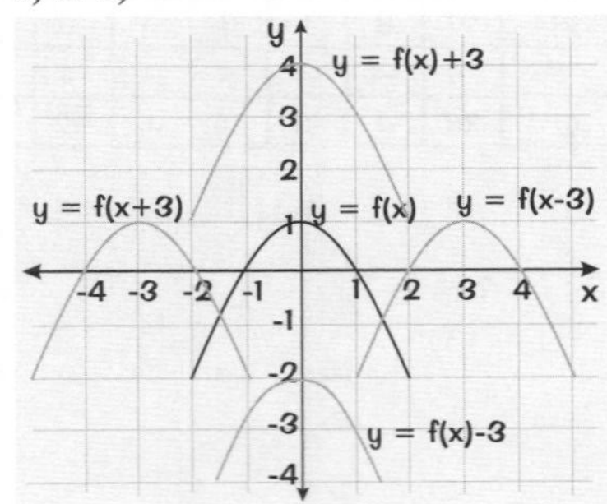

e) and **f)**

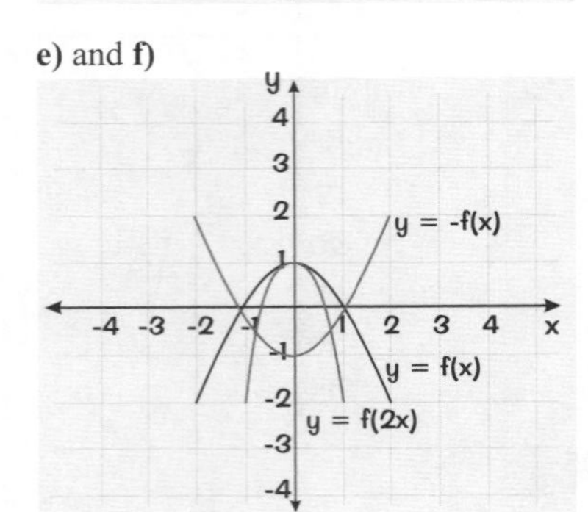

g) and **h)**

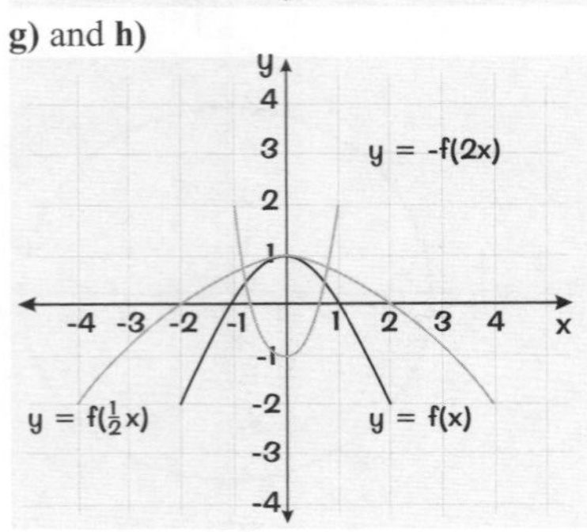

Q2 a) to **d)**

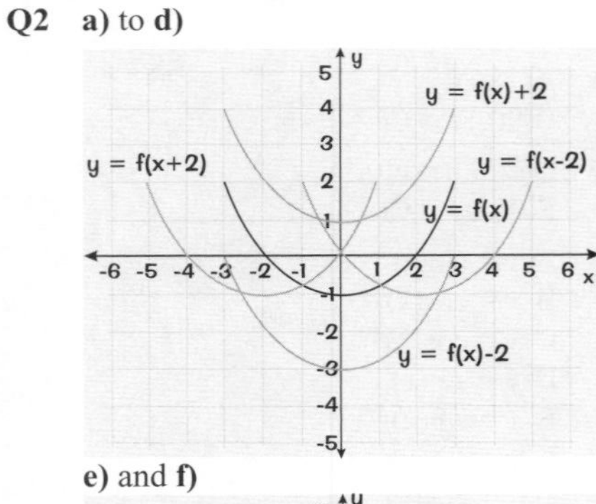

e) and **f)**

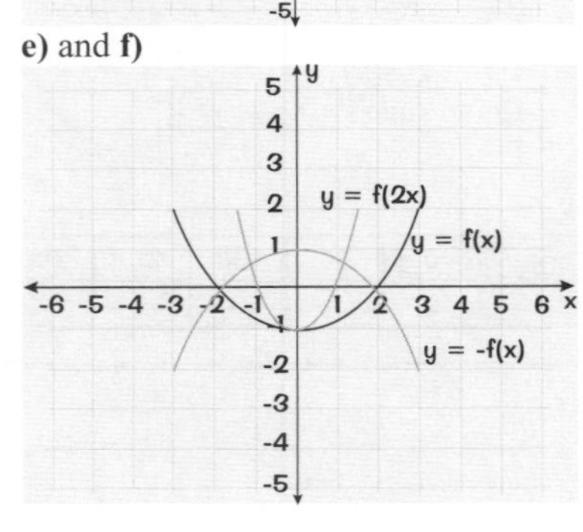

g) to **i)**

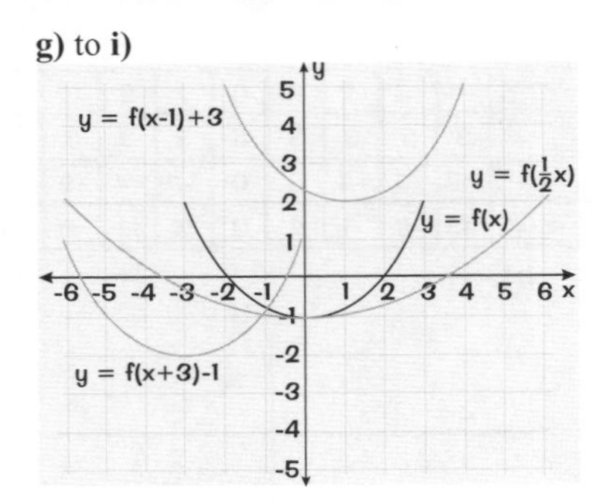

Q3 a) and **b)**

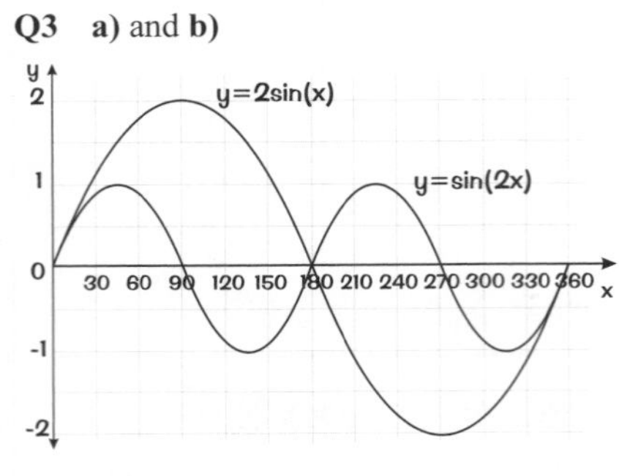

Q4 a) and **b)**

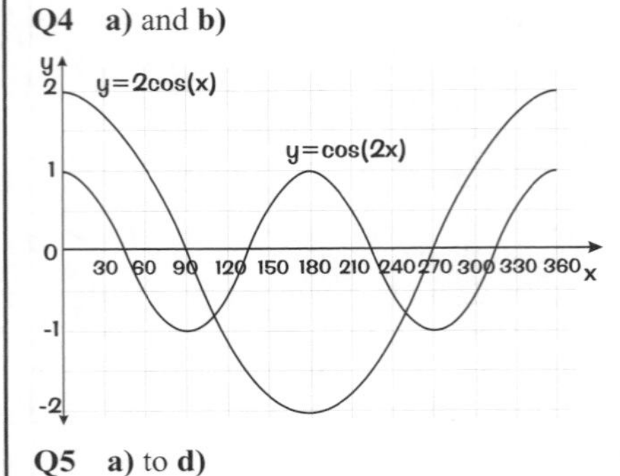

Q5 a) to **d)**

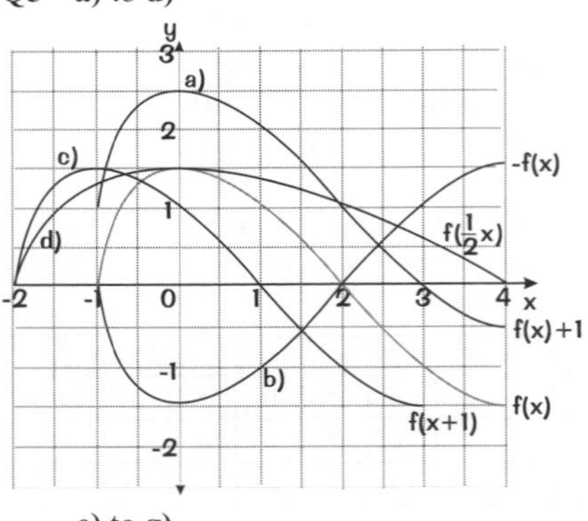

e) to **g)**

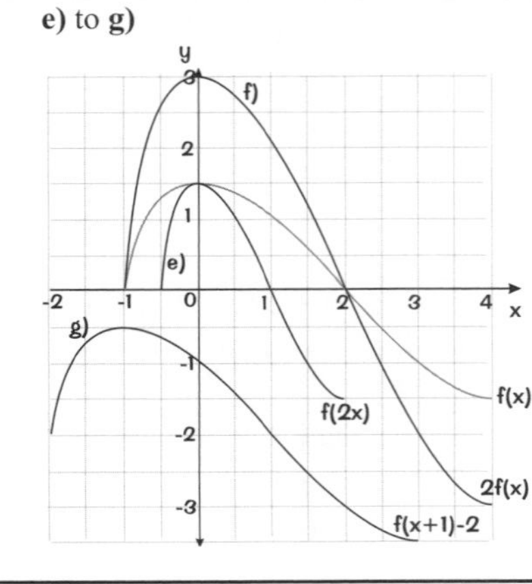

Real-Life Graphs P.61

Q1 1 D
2 B
3 A
4 E
5 C

Q2 **a)** Provider A: $P = 0.03N + 5$
Provider B: $P = 0.05N$
b) i) Provider A: £17; Provider B: £20
ii) Provider A: £26; Provider B: £35
c) 250 units

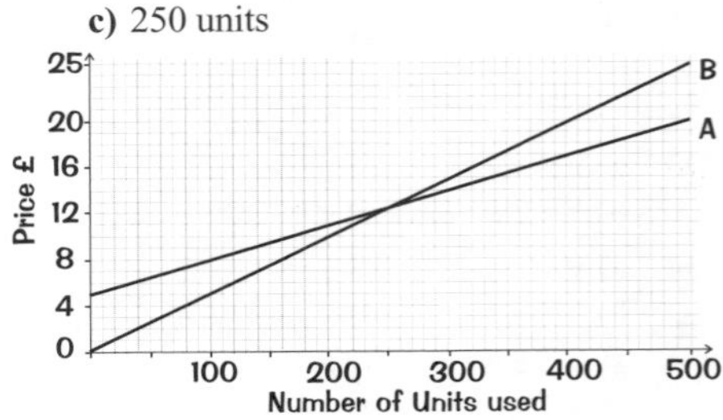

Section Four — Geometry and Measure

Geometry P.62-P.63

Q1 **a)** $x = 47°$
b) $y = 154°$
c) $z = 22°$
d) $p = 35°$, $q = 45°$

Q2 **a)** $a = 146°$
b) $m = 131°$, $z = 48°$
c) $x = 68°$, $p = 112°$
d) $s = 20°$, $t = 90°$

Q3 **a)** $x = 96°$, $p = 38°$
b) $a = 108°$, $b = 23°$, $c = 95°$
c) $d = 120°$, $e = 60°$, $f = 60°$, $g = 120°$
d) $h = 155°$, $i = 77.5°$, $j = 102.5°$, $k = 77.5°$

Q4 **a)** $b = 70°$ $c = 30°$
$d = 50°$ $e = 60°$
$f = 150°$
b) $g = 21°$ $h = 71°$
$i = 80°$ $j = 38°$
$k = 92°$
c) $l = 35°$ $m = 145°$
$n = 55°$ $p = 125°$

Q5 **a)** $x = 162°$ $y = 18°$
b) $x = 87°$ $y = 93°$
$z = 93°$
c) $a = 30°$ $2a = 60°$
$5a = 150°$ $4a = 120°$

Q6 **a)** $a = 141°$, $b = 141°$, $c = 39°$,
$d = 141°$, $e = 39°$
b) $a = 47°$, $b = 47°$, $c = 133°$,
$d = 43°$, $e = 43°$
c) $m = 140°$, $n = 140°$, $p = 134°$,
$q = 46°$, $r = 40°$

Answers: P.64 — P.68

Polygons P.64-P.65

Q1 Isosceles.

Q2

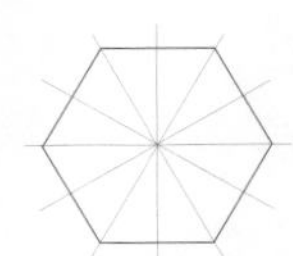

order of rotational symmetry = 6.

Q3 $540° - (100° + 104° + 120°)$
$= 216°$ for two equal angles
$\therefore 1$ angle $= 108°$

Q4 **a)** $90° + 60° = 150°$

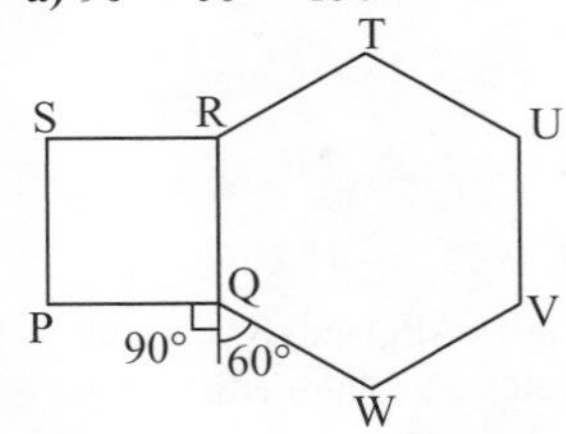

b)

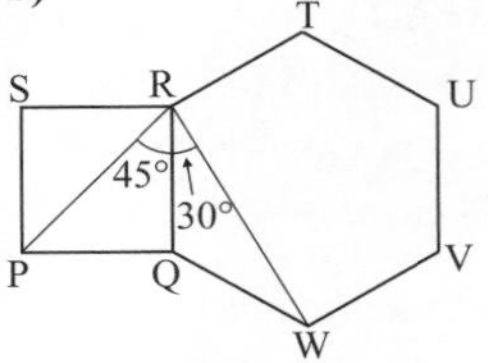

$\angle PRW = 75°$

c) $180 - (360/n) = 150$
$180n - 360 = 150n$
$30n = 360 \Rightarrow n = 12$

Q5 **a)** Interior angle = 165°
b) Exterior angle = $180° - 165° = 15°$
Sum of exterior angles = 15×24
$= 360°$

Q6 **a)**

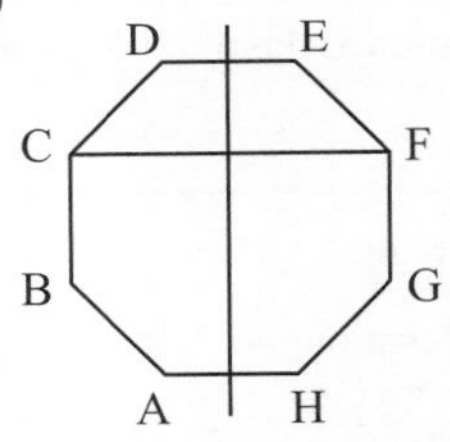

b) Angle CDE = angle DEF
$= \dfrac{(8-2)180}{8} = 135°$
so angle EFC $= \dfrac{360 - 2(135)}{2} = 45°$
or exterior angle = 45° = angle EFC, alternate angles.

Q7 $(n-2)180 = 2520$, $n = 16$

Q8 **a)** $\frac{360}{5} = 72°$
b) $\frac{180-72}{2} = 54°$
c) **i)** 90°
ii) 36°

Q9 **a)** Angles at a point sum to 360°, hence $m + m + r = 360°$.
Angles in a pentagon sum to 540°. We know two angles are 90°, so we are left with 360°. The only angles left are m, m and r so $m + m + r$ must equal 360°.
b) r°.

Q10 **a)** $(\frac{360}{5}) \div 2 = 36°$
b) $OX = 5 \cos 36 = 4.045$ cm.
Hence $MX = 5 - 4.045 = 0.96$ cm.

Symmetry P.66

Q1

a) b) c)

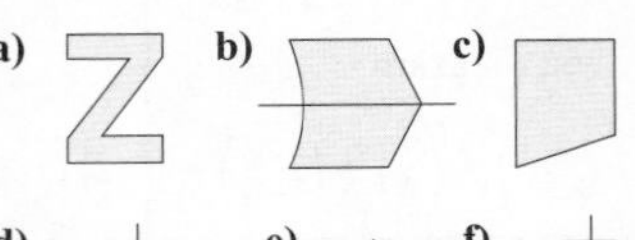

d) e) f)

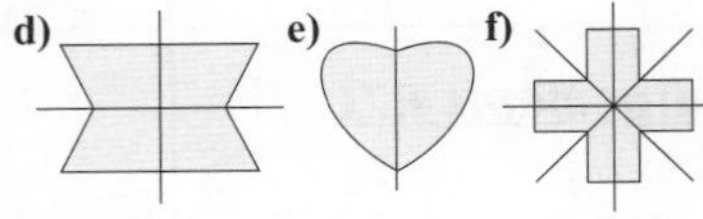

Q2 **a)** 6 **b)** 8
c) 5 **d)** 3

Q3

Order of Rotation: 1, 2, 1, 1

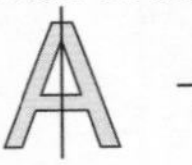

Order of Rotation: 1, 1, 2

Circle Geometry P.67-P.68

Q1 **a)** BAD = 80° (opposite angle C in cyclic quadrilateral)
b) EAB = 180 – 80 – 30 = 70°

Q2 **a)** BD = 5 cm (as the tangents BD and CD are equal).
b) Angle COD = 70° (= 180° – (20° + 90°)), since the tangent CD meets the radius OC at an angle of 90°.
c) Angle COB = 140° (since angle BOD equals angle COD).
d) Angle CAB = 70° (since the angle at the centre (COB) is twice the angle at the edge (CAB)).

Q3 **a)** BOE = 106° (angle at centre)
b) ACE = 32° (angle in opposite segment)

Q4 **a)** ACD = 70° (angle in opposite segment)
b) BAD = 180 – (30 + 70) = 80° (opposite angles of a cyclic quadrilateral total 180°)

Q5 **a)** Angles in the same segment.
b) $3x + 40 = 6x - 50$
$90 = 3x$
$30 = x$
angle ABD $= 3(30) + 40 = 130°$

Q6 There are 2 ways of answering this question.

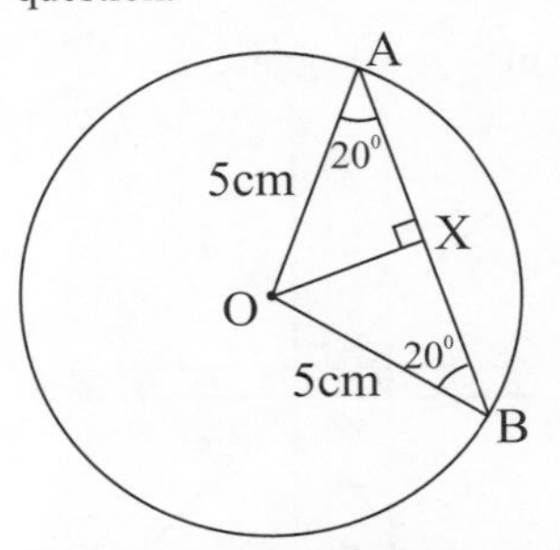

The perpendicular bisector of the chord bisects it at X so,
$\cos 20° = \frac{AX}{5} \Rightarrow$
AX = 4.698 and
AB = 9.40 cm.

or by the sine rule $\frac{AB}{\sin 140} = \frac{5}{\sin 20}$
$AB = \frac{5 \sin 140}{\sin 20} = 9.40$ cm

Q7 **a)** Angle ABD = 70° (angle at centre = 2 × angle at circumference)
b) Angle ABC = 90° (angle in semicircle)
c) Angle DBC = 20° (90° – 70°)

Q8 **a)** 90° (angle in a semicircle)
b) The angle at A = 90° (tangent and radius are perpendicular). The third angle in the triangle is $180 - 90 - 23 = 67°$ and so $x = 90 - 67 = 23°$.
Or, by alternative segment theorem: x = angle ABC = 23°.

Q9 **a)** With AD as a chord, angle ABD = ACD = 30° (same segment); angle AXB = 85° (vertically opposite angles). The third angles must be the same in both triangles so the triangles must be similar.
b) Ratio of lengths $= \frac{4}{8} = \frac{1}{2}$
so XB = 7.25 cm
c) angle BDC = 180 – 85 – 30 = 65°

Q10 **a)** 90° (angle in a semicircle)
b) Pythagoras is needed here but in the form
$AC^2 + 3^2 = 10^2$
$AC^2 = 100 - 9 = 91$
AC = 9.54 cm
c) AD = 5 cm so DC = 9.54 – 5 = 4.54 cm then Pythagoras again gives
$(4.54)^2 + 3^2 = (DOB)^2$
$20.606 + 9 = (DOB)^2$
So DOB = 5.44 cm

Answers: P.69 — P.73

The Four Transformations P.69-P.70

Q1 **a)** to **e)** — see diagram.

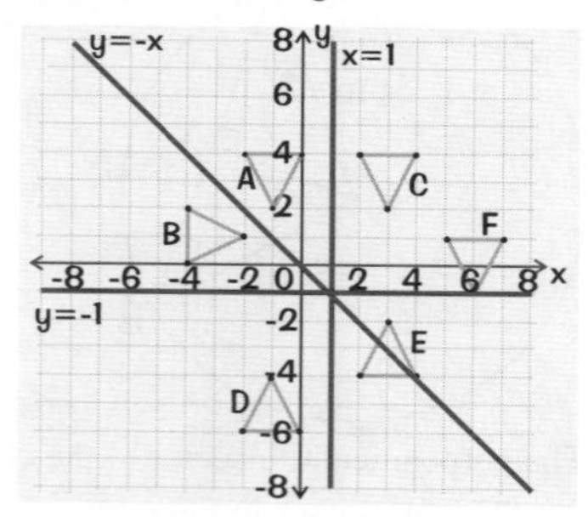

f) Rotation of 180°, centre (3, 0)

Q2 **a), b), d), e)** — see diagram

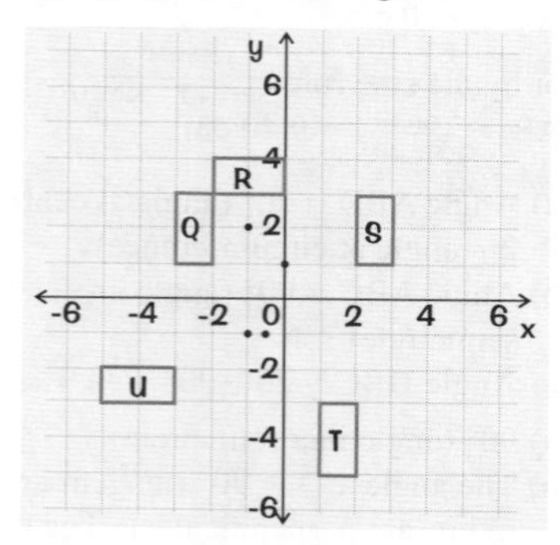

c) Rotation 180° about (0, 2).

f) 90° rotation anticlockwise about $\left(-\frac{1}{2}, -\frac{1}{2}\right)$.
Or, 90° rotation clockwise about (–2, –6).

Q3 **a), b)** — see diagram.

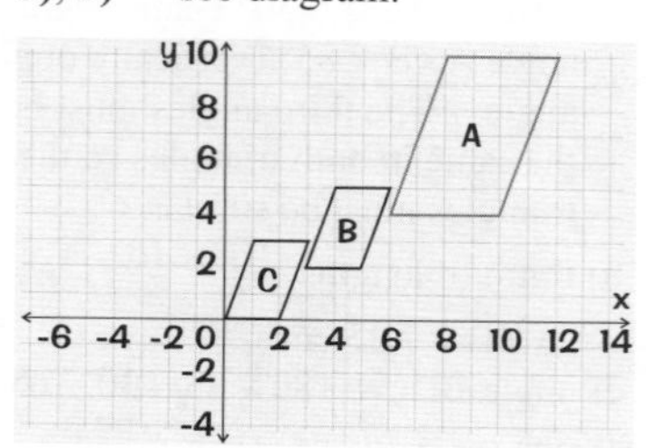

c) Ratio of areas C:A = 1:4

Q4 **a), b), c)** — see diagram.

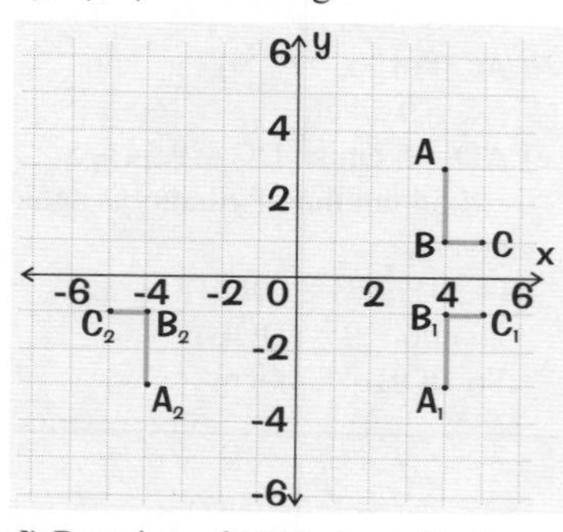

d) Rotation of 180° about (0, 0)

Q5 **a)**

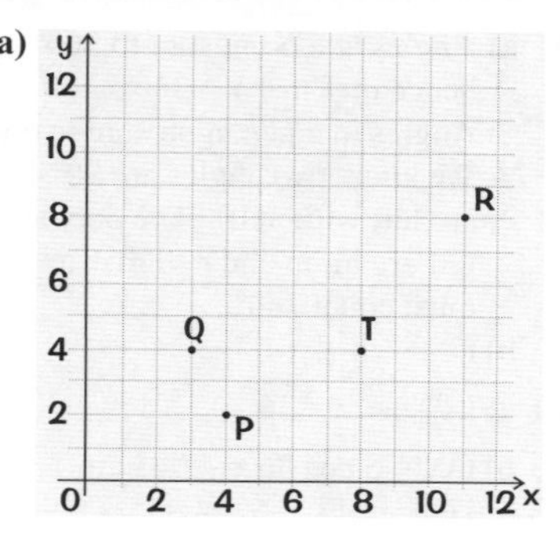

b) $\overrightarrow{QO} = \begin{pmatrix} -3 \\ -4 \end{pmatrix}$

$T = \begin{pmatrix} 11 \\ 8 \end{pmatrix} + \begin{pmatrix} -3 \\ -4 \end{pmatrix} = \begin{pmatrix} 8 \\ 4 \end{pmatrix}$

see diagram

c) $\begin{pmatrix} -1 \\ 2 \end{pmatrix} + \begin{pmatrix} 8 \\ 4 \end{pmatrix} + \begin{pmatrix} -3 \\ -4 \end{pmatrix} + \begin{pmatrix} -4 \\ -2 \end{pmatrix} = \begin{pmatrix} 0 \\ 0 \end{pmatrix}$

Enlargements P.71

Q1 **a) & b)**

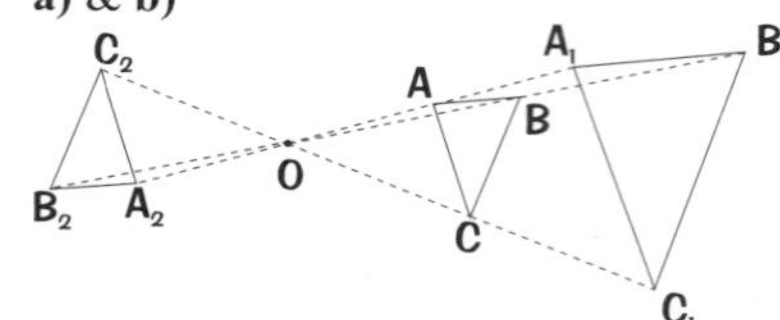

Q2 **a)** 2 end faces 2 × (2 × 3) = 12 cm²
2 side faces 2 × (5 × 3) = 30 cm²
Top & bottom 2 × (5 × 2) = 20 cm²
Total = 62 cm²

b) SF for length = 1:4
SF for area = 1:16
new area = 62 × 16 = 992 cm²

Q3 Widths in ratio 2:3, so volumes in ratio 8:27.
Volume = 30 × $\frac{27}{8}$ = 101 litres

Q4 **a)** volume = $\frac{1}{3}\pi(100^2)(100)$ = 1047198 cm³ = 1.05 m³

b) 50 cm

c) ratio = 1:2³ = 1:8

d) Volume of small cone = 1.05 × $\frac{1}{8}$ = 0.131 m³

e) volume of portion left = 1.05 – 0.131 = 0.919
so ratio = 0.919:0.131 = $\frac{0.919}{0.131}$:1 = 7:1

Congruent and Similar Shapes P.72

Q1 ABC and DFE are congruent by SAS (same size angles and side lengths).

Q2

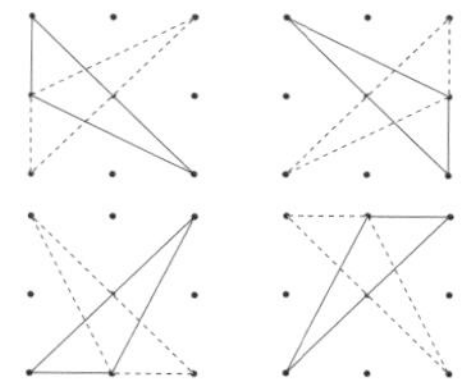

Hence 7 ways to draw another.

Q3 **a)** Angle A shared. Parallel lines make corresponding angles equal so the triangles are similar by AAA.

b) Ratio of lengths given by $\frac{AB}{AD} = \frac{12}{20} = \frac{3}{5}$

So $x = 25 \times \frac{3}{5} = 15$ cm

Also $\frac{y+10}{y} = \frac{5}{3}$

=> $2y = 30$, $y = 15$ cm

Q4 **a)** Triangles APQ and STC (both isosceles and share either angle A or C)

b) Ratio AC:AQ = 24:7.5 = 3.2:1 so
AP = 15 × $\frac{1}{3.2}$ = 4.6875 cm
PT = 24 – 2 (4.6875) = 14.625 cm.

c) Using $\frac{1}{2}$(base)(height) = $\frac{1}{2}$(24)(9) = 108 cm²

d) Scale factor = $\frac{1}{3.2}$
Area scale factor = $\frac{1}{10.24}$
Area of triangle APQ = 108 × $\frac{1}{10.24}$ = 10.5 cm²

e) 108 – 2 (10.5) = 87 cm²

Q5 **a)** All lengths must be enlarged in the same ratio for them to be similar.

b) 4 litres

Projections P.73

Q1 **a)** Front elevation:

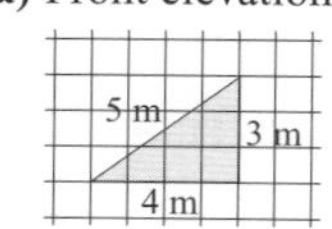

b) Side elevation:

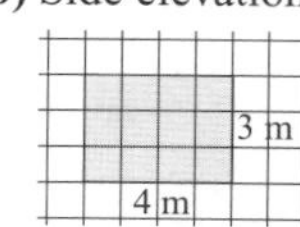

c) Plan:

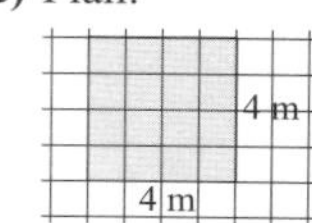

Q2

Answers: P.73 — P.78

Q3

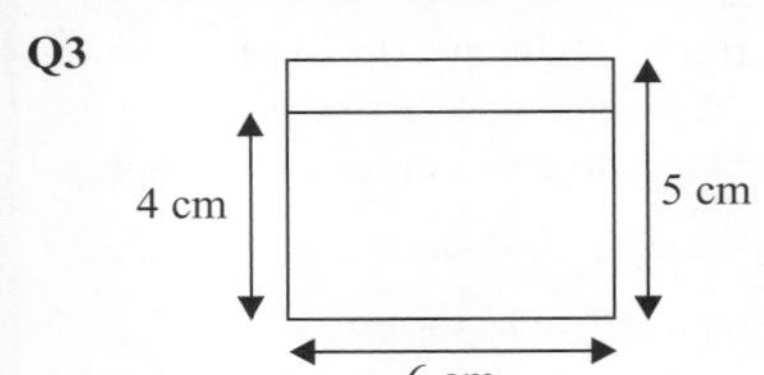

Q4

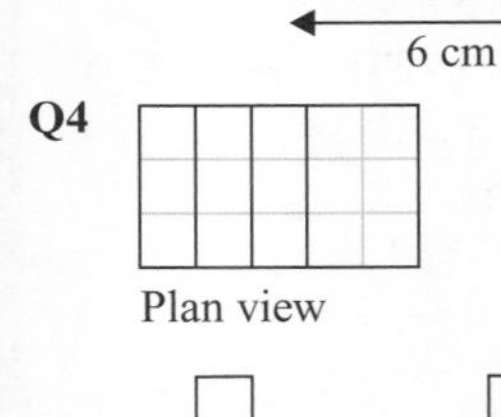

Plan view

Front elevation   Side elevation

Perimeter and Area P.74-P.76

Q1 Area 24 cm², perimeter 20 cm

Q2 Area 25 cm², perimeter 20 cm

Q3 **a)** Area = $(4 \times 4) - (1 \times 2 + \frac{1}{2} \times \pi \times 1^2) + \frac{1}{2} \times \pi \times 2^2$
$= 16 - 3.5708 + 6.2832$
$= 18.7$ m² (1 d.p.)

b) Three 1 litre tins of paint are needed for two coats.

c) Perimeter = $1 + 1 + (\frac{1}{2} \times \pi \times 2) + 1 + 1 + 4 + (\frac{1}{2} \times \pi \times 4) + 4$
$= 12 + 3\pi = 21.4$ m (1 d.p.)

Q4 **a)** l = 24, w = 12, area = 288 m²

b) 1 Carpet tile = 0.50 × 0.50 = 0.25 m²
So 288 m² ÷ 0.25 = 1152 tiles are required.

c) £4.99 per m² => £4.99 for 4 tiles
Total cost = (1152 ÷ 4) × 4.99
= £1437.12

Q5 Area = 120 cm²

Q6 Each square = 0.6 m × 0.6 m = 0.36 m².
Total area of material = 6 × 0.36 = 2.16 m²

Q7 Perimeter = $4 \times \sqrt{9000}$
= 379.47 m (2 d.p.)
Natasha ran: 11 × 379.47
= 4200 m (to nearest 100 m)

Q8 48 ÷ 5 = 9.6 m length. Area of 1 roll = 11 m × 0.5 m = 5.5 m².
48 m² ÷ 5.5 m² = $8\frac{8}{11}$ rolls of turf required. Of course 9 should be ordered.

Q9 Base length = 4773 ÷ 43 = 111 mm.

Q10 Area of metal blade = ½ × 35 × (70 + 155) = 3937.5 mm²

Q11 Area of larger triangle
= ½ × 14.4 × 10 = 72 cm².
Area of inner triangle
= ½ × 5.76 × 4 = 11.52 cm².
Area of metal used for a bracket = 72 – 11.52 = 60.48 cm² so NO, bracket is too heavy for the fixing.

Q12 T_1: ½ × 8 × 16 = 64 m²
Tr_1: ½ × 8 × (8 + 16) = 96 m²
Tr_2: ½ × 4 × (8 + 12) = 40 m²
T_2: ½ × 8 × 12 = 48 m²
Total area of glass sculpture = 248 m²

Q13 Area = ½ × 8.2 × 4.1 = 16.81 m²
Perimeter = 10.8 + 4.5 + 8.2 = 23.5m.

Q14 **a)** Area of each isosceles triangle = ½ × 2.3 × 3.2 = 3.68 m²

b) Area of each side = $(\sqrt{3.2^2 + 1.15^2}) \times 4 = 13.6$ m²
Groundsheet = 2.3 × 4 = 9.2 m²

c) Total material = 2 × 3.68 + 9.2 + 2 × 13.6 = 43.8 m²

Q15

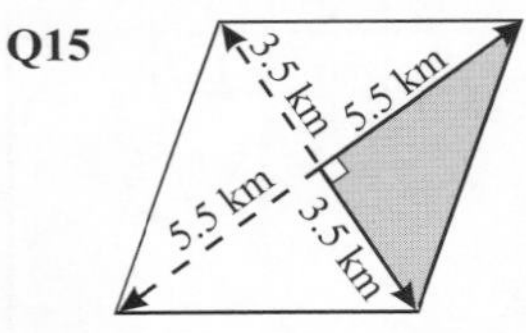

Area = ½ × product of diagonals
= ½ × 7 × 11 = 38.5 km².

Q16 B = major sector
C = chord
D = tangent

Q17 **a)** 117.607 m²
b) 45.216 = 45 m to 2 s.f.
c) 46.5 m to 1dp.
d) 14.152 cm² to 3dp.

Q18 **a)** Area = area of a full circle radius 10 cm. $A = \pi r^2 = 3.14 \times 10^2$
= 314 cm².
Circumference = π × D = 3.14 × 20
= 62.8 cm.
Perimeter = 62.8 + 20 = 82.8 cm

b) Area = (area of a full circle radius 15 cm) + (area of a rectangle 15 × 30 cm) = $(\pi \times 15^2) + (15 \times 30)$
= 1156.5 cm².
Perimeter = (Circumference of a full circle radius 15 cm) + 15 +15 (two shorter sides of rectangle) = (π × 30) + 30 = 124.2 cm.

c) Area = Outer semi circle – Inner semi circle = 510.25 m².
Perimeter = ½ Circumference of larger + ½ Circumference of inner + 5 + 5 = ½ × π × 70 + ½ × π × 60 + 10 = 214.1 m.

Q19 **a)** ABDC = $\frac{60}{360} \times \pi(30)^2 - \frac{60}{360} \times \pi(20)^2$
= 261.8 mm²

b) $2(\frac{1}{2}\pi 5^2) = 78.5$ mm².
Hence 261.8 + 78.5 = 340.3 mm².

Q20 **a)** $80/360 \times \pi 5^2 = 17.45$ cm²

b) Area of triangle AOB = $\frac{1}{2} \times 5 \times 5 \times \sin 80 = 12.31$ cm².
Shaded Area = 17.45 – 12.31
= 5.14 cm²

Surface Area P.77-P.78

Q1 **a) - c)**

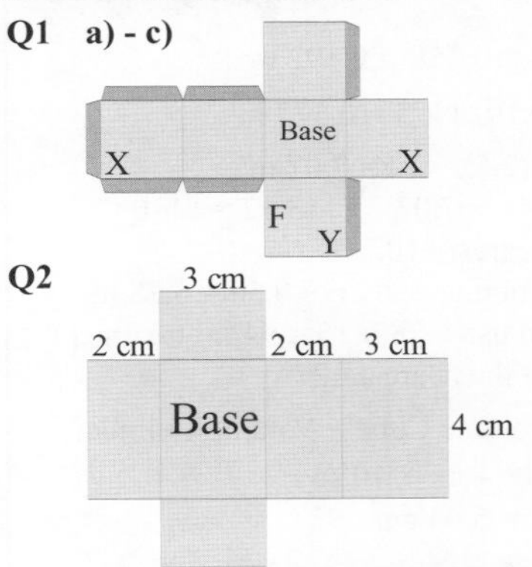

Q2

3 cm
2 cm   2 cm   3 cm
Base   4 cm

Other arrangements are possible.

Q3 **a)** H, F and D

b) Line symmetry through lines AF, DH, BG and CE. Rotational symmetry of order 4.

c) 5 faces and vertices, 8 edges.

Q4 **a)** I
b) 64 cm²
c) 64 × 6 = 384 cm²
d)

Q5 Net B

Q6 No, Hannah would need more than 603 cm².

Q7 Surface area = $4 \times \pi \times 3^2$
= 113.10 cm² (to 2 d.p)

Q8 Surface area of cone = $\pi rl + \pi r^2$
$= (\pi \times 1.5 \times 8) + (\pi \times 1.5^2)$
= 44.77 cm² (to 2 d.p)
Height of triangular prism = $\sqrt{3^2 - 1.5^2}$
$= \sqrt{6.75} = 2.598...$ cm
Surface area of triangular prism =
$2(\frac{1}{2} \times 3 \times 2.598...) + 3(3 \times 8)$
= 79.79 cm² (to 2 d.p.)
Therefore the triangular prism has the largest surface area.

Q9 Surface area of hemisphere =
$\pi r^2 + \frac{1}{2}(4\pi r^2)$
$75\pi = 3\pi r^2$
$r^2 = 25$, radius = 5 cm

Q10 $AB^2 = 2^2 + 1.5^2$ AB = 2.5 m
1 panel on roof = ½AB × $\frac{5}{2}$
= 1.25 × 2.5 = 3.125 m²
Front of greenhouse = (2.5 × 4) + (½ × 4 × 1.5) = 13 m²
Total = 3.125 + 13 = 16.125 m²

Answers: P.79 — P.84

Volume P.79-P.81

Q1 **a)** $\frac{1}{2}\pi(0.35)^2 = 0.192\ m^2$
b) $0.1924 \times 3 = 0.577\ m^3$

Q2 **a)** $\pi(2.5^2 - 2^2) = 7.07\ m^2$
£16 × 7.07 = £113.12 = £110 to nearest £10.
b) Volume = $\pi(2)^2 \times 0.50 = 6.28\ m^3$ so use 6.28 × 15 = 94 ml treatment to the nearest ml.

Q3 **a)** Volume Cube = Volume Cylinder
$10^3 = \pi r^2 \times 10$ so $r^2 = \frac{10^2}{\pi}$, $r = 5.64$ cm
b) S.A. of cylinder = $2\pi rh + 2\pi r^2 = 2\pi \times 5.64... \times 10 + 2\pi \times (5.64...)^2 = 554.49\ cm^2$

Q4 **a)** $\pi(5)^2(16) = 1257\ cm^3$
b) $\pi(5)^2 h = 600$
$h = \frac{600}{25\pi} = 7.64$ cm

Q5 $(3)(3)(0.5) - \pi(0.7)^2(0.5) = 3.73\ cm^3$

Q6 Volume = $\frac{1}{3} \times (230 \times 230) \times 139$
$= 2\ 451\ 033\ m^3$

Q7 $(\pi \times (2)^2 \times 110) +$
$(½(14 + 20) \times 6 \times 20) = 3422.30\ cm^3$
$2 \times 3422.30 = 6844.60\ cm^3 = 6.84$ l

Q8 **a)** $(60)(30) + (30)(120) = 5400\ cm^2$
b) $5400 \times 100 = 540000\ cm^3 = 0.54\ m^3$

Q9 **a) i)** B = (0, 8, 5) **ii)** D = (4, 8, 0)
b) $(½ \times 4 \times 5) \times 8 = 80\ units^3$

Q10 Volume = $\frac{4}{3}\pi r^3 = \frac{4}{3} \times \pi \times 15^3$
$= 14137\ cm^3$

Q11 **a)** $\frac{1}{2}(\frac{4}{3}\pi(1.3)^3) + \pi(1.3)^2 \times 1.8$
$+ \frac{1}{3}\pi(1.3)^2 \times 1.2 = 16.28\ cm^3$
b) Volume of sand in hemisphere and cone parts remain the same so change is in cylindrical part. Therefore $h + 0.3 = 1.8$, $h = 1.5$ cm.
c) Volume of sand transferred =
$\frac{1}{2}(\frac{4}{3}\pi(1.3)^3) + \pi(1.3)^2 \times 1.5$
$= 12.57\ cm^3$
Time Taken = $\frac{12.57}{0.05} \approx 251$ secs.
= 4 minutes 11 secs

Q12 **a)** Volume of ice cream
$= \frac{1}{3}\pi(R^2H - r^2h) + \frac{1}{2}(\frac{4}{3}\pi R^3)$
$= \frac{1}{3}\pi(2.5^2 \times 10 - 1^2 \times 4)$
$+ \frac{1}{2}(\frac{4}{3}\pi \times 2.5^3)$
$= 93.99\ cm^3$ of ice cream.

b) Outer surface area of cone
$= \pi Rl$
Using pythagoras,
$l^2 = 10^2 + 2.5^2 = 106.25$,
$l = 10.3$ cm. So S.A. =
$\pi \times 2.5 \times 10.3 = 81.0\ cm^2$

Q13 Vol. increase is a cylinder of height 4.5 cm. So vol. increase =
$\pi(5)^2 \times 4.5 = 353.4\ cm^3$.
Volume of each marble = $\frac{353.4}{200}$
$= 1.767\ cm^3$
$\frac{4}{3}\pi r^3 = 1.767 \Rightarrow r = 0.75$ cm

Q14 **a)** $x(3 - x)(5 - x)\ m^3$ or $x^3 - 8x^2 + 15x$
b)

X	0	1	2	3
V	0	8	6	0

c)

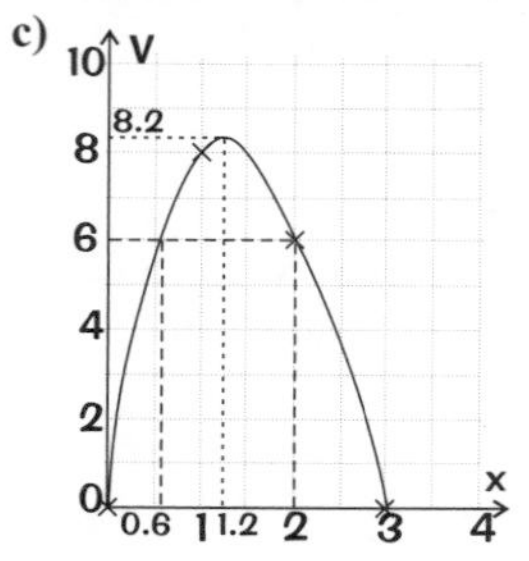

d) about $8.2\ m^3$
e) ends 2(1.2)(1.8) = 4.32 +
side faces 2(1.2)(3.8) = 9.12 +
tops 2(3.8)(1.8) = 13.68
So area is about $27.12m^2$
f) $x = 2$ or $x = 0.6$
If $x = 0.6$:
ends 2(0.6)(2.4) = 2.88 +
side faces 2(0.6)(4.4) = 5.28 +
tops 2(2.4)(4.4) = 21.12
$29.28m^2$
If $x = 2$:
ends 2(2)(1) = 4 +
side faces 2(2)(3) = 12 +
tops 2(1)(3) = 6
$22m^2$
Maximum Total S.A. $\approx 29.28\ m^2$

Speed, Distance and Time P.82-P.83

Q1 60 km/h

Q2 165 miles

Q3 2 hours 40 minutes

Q4

Distance travelled	Time taken	Average Speed
210 km	3 hrs	70 km/h
135 miles	4 hrs 30 mins	30 mph
105 km	2 hrs 30 mins	42 km/h
9 miles	45 mins	12 mph
640 km	48 mins	800 km/h
70 miles	1 hr 10 mins	60 mph

Q5 **a)** 100/11 = 9.09 m/s (to 2d.p)
b) 32.73 km/h

Q6 7 minutes to go 63 miles so 540 mph.

Q7 $\frac{260}{71}$ hours = 3.66 hrs ≈ 3 hrs 40 min
07.05 to 10.30 is 3 hrs 25 mins.
Journey takes over 3 hrs 25 mins so No.

Q8 **a)** 98.9 mph (to 3 s.f.)
b) 72.56 seconds
c) 99.2 mph (to 3 s.f.)

Q9 **a)** 2.77 + 1.96 + 0.6 = 5.33 hrs (to 3 s.f.) = 5 hours 20 mins
b) 250 miles
c) 46.9 mph (to 3 s.f.)

Q10 2.15pm

Q11 **a)** 2.23 hrs (2 hrs 14 mins)
b) 1 hr 49 mins + 10 mins = 1 hr 59 mins
c) 1346 and 1401

Q12 The first athlete ran at 16000 ÷ (60 × 60) = 4.44 m/s, so was faster than the second athlete (at 4 m/s). The first athlete would take 37.5 mins to run 10 km; the second would take 41.7 mins.

Q13 **a)** 487.5 km
b) 920.8 km
c) 497 km/h

Q14 **a)** 8.13 m/s
b) 7.30 m/s

Q15 **a)** 220 km
b) 5 mins

Q16 180 m at 42 mph takes 4 hrs 17 mins.
180 m at 64 mph takes 2 hrs 49 mins.
So it stops for 1 hr 28 mins.

Q17 **a)** 4.8 m/s
b) 14.4 m/s
c) 14.4 m/s
d) 17.3 km/h, 51.8 km/h, 51.8 km/h.

Q18 2.05 mins, 2.07 mins, 2.13 mins.

Density P.84

Q1 **a)** $0.75\ g/cm^3$
b) $0.6\ g/cm^3$
c) $0.8\ g/cm^3$
d) $700\ kg/m^3 = 0.7\ g/cm^3$

Q2 **a)** 62.4 g
b) 96 g
c) 3744 g (3.744 kg)
d) 75 g

Q3 **a)** $625\ cm^3$
b) $89.3\ cm^3$ (to 3 s.f.)
c) $27778\ cm^3$ (27800 to 3 s.f.)
d) $2500\ cm^3$

Q4 34.71 g

Q5 $20968\ cm^3$

Answers: P.84 — P.89

Q6 Vol. = 5000 cm^3 = 5 litres

Q7 1.05 g/cm^3

Q8 **a)** SR flour 1.16 g/cm^3; granary flour 1.19 g/cm^3
b) 378 ml

Distance-Time Graphs P.85

Q1 **a)** 85 mins
b) 80 mins
c) 16.9 mph
d) 57.6 mph
e) No, because the total driving time is 80 minutes.

Q2 **a)** A 80.0 km/h, fastest.
B 57.1 km/h
C 66.7 km/h
D 44.4 km/h
E 50.0 km/h
b) steepest slope was fastest, least steep slope was slowest.

Q3 **a)** B **b)** 3¾ mins
c) B
d) **i)** 267 m/min **ii)** 16.0 km/h
e) C was the fastest; 700 m/min or 42 km/h

Q4

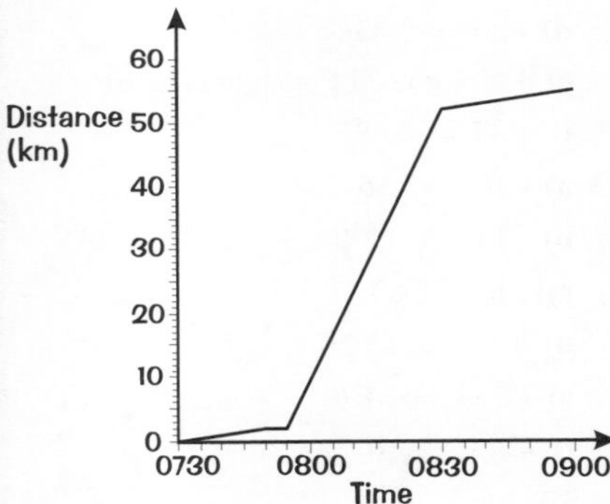

He waited for 5 mins.

Unit Conversions P.86-P.87

Q1 1400 cm^3

Q2

a) 200 cm	**i)** 0.65 km
b) 33 mm	**j)** 9000 g
c) 4000 g	**k)** 0.007 kg
d) 0.6 kg	**l)** 0.95 kg
e) 48 in	**m)** 72 in
f) 3 ft	**n)** 80 oz
g) 7 ft 3 in	**o)** 100 yd 1 ft
h) 2 lb 11 oz	**p)** 6000 mm

Q3 147 kg × 2.2 = 323.4 lbs

Q4 14 gallons = 14 × 4.5 = 63 litres

Q5 9 stone 4 lbs = 130 lbs
130 lbs ÷ 2.2 = 59.1 kg

Q6 Barry cycled 30 miles = 30 × 1.6 = 48 km. So Barbara cycled furthest.

Q7 **a)** 11 in = 11 × 2.5 = 27.5 cm
b) 275 mm

Q8 **a)** 21 feet = 21 × 12 = 252 in
b) 21 feet = 21 ÷ 3 = 7 yd
c) 21 feet = 21 × 0.3 = 6.3 m
d) 6.3 m = 630 cm
e) 630 cm = 6300 mm
f) 6.3 m = 0.0063 km

Q9 5 lb = 5 ÷ 2.2 = 2.3 kg. So Dick needs to buy 3 bags of sugar.

Q10 **a)** 60 kg = 60 × 2.2 = 132 lbs
b) 132 lbs = 132 × 16 = 2112 oz
c) 10 st. = 140 lbs ÷ 2.2 = 63.6 kg, so Sylvester can lift most.

Q11 **a)** (40 ÷ 5) × 8 = 64 km/h
b) 18.8 × 3600 = 67 680 m/h
67 680 ÷ 1000 = 67.68 km/h
67.68 – 64 = 3.68 km/h, so the car was 3.68 km/h over the speed limit.
c) 1750 × 3600 = 6 300 000 cm/h
6 300 000 ÷ 100 000 = 63 km/h
64 – 63 = 1, so the car was 1 km/h under the speed limit.

Q12 **a)** 900 ÷ 100 = 9 cm^2
b) 15 × 1 000 000 = 15 000 000 mm^2
c) 4 × 10 000 = 40 000 cm^2
d) 500 ÷ 10 000 = 0.05 m^2
e) 38 × 100 = 3800 mm^2
f) 860 000 ÷ 1 000 000 = 0.86 m^2

Q13 **a)** 2500 × 1 000 000 = 2 500 000 000 cm^3
b) 2500 × 1 000 000 000 = 2 500 000 000 000 mm^3

Q14 682 000 ÷ 1000 = 682 cm^3
The volume of the brain is bigger than the volume of the skull so the scientist can't be right.

Q15 **a)** £52
b) £35 = €42, so he does have enough money.
c) 1 kg ≈ 2.2 lbs, so 15 ÷ 2.2 = €6.82/lb
€26 ≈ £22, so €1 ≈ £0.85
6.82 × 0.85 = 5.80, therefore it costs £5.80 per 1b.

Q16 **a)** 12-13 miles
b) 43-44 miles
c) 47-49 km

Loci and Construction P.88-P.89

Q1

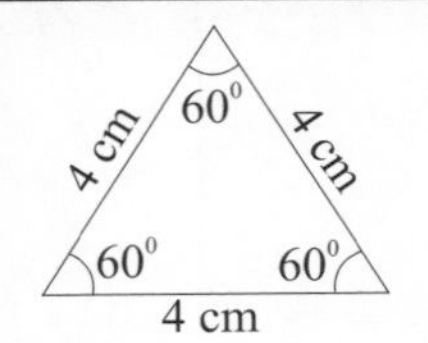

Not to scale

Q2

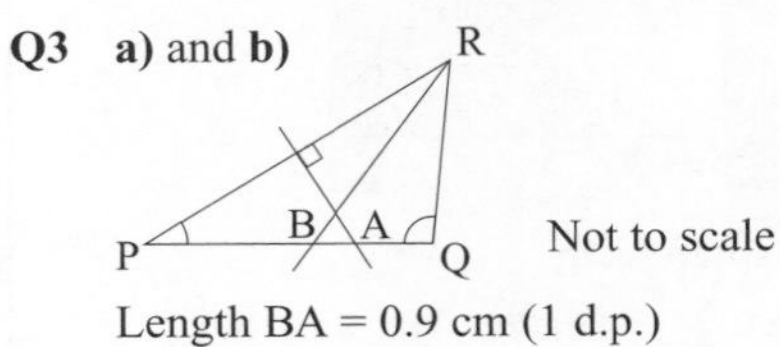

Not to scale

Q3 **a)** and **b)**

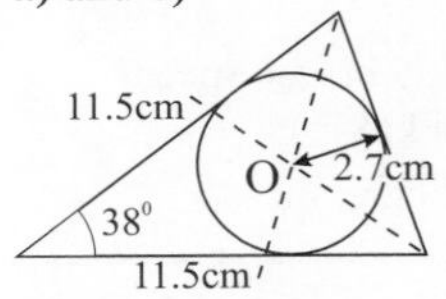

Not to scale

Length BA = 0.9 cm (1 d.p.)

Q4

Not to scale

Q5 **a)** and **b)**

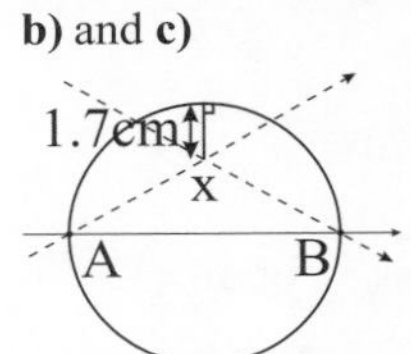

Not to scale

Radius of the circle = 2.7 cm

Q6 **a)** A circle with diameter AB.
b) and **c)**

Not to scale

d) The ship comes 1.7 cm = 0.85 km from the rocks.

Q7

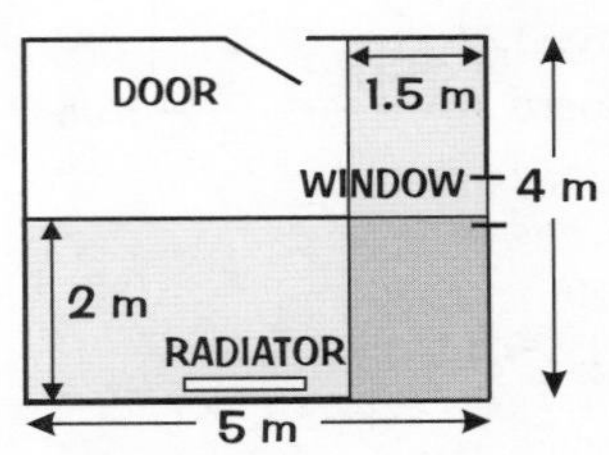

Not to scale

Q8 **a)**

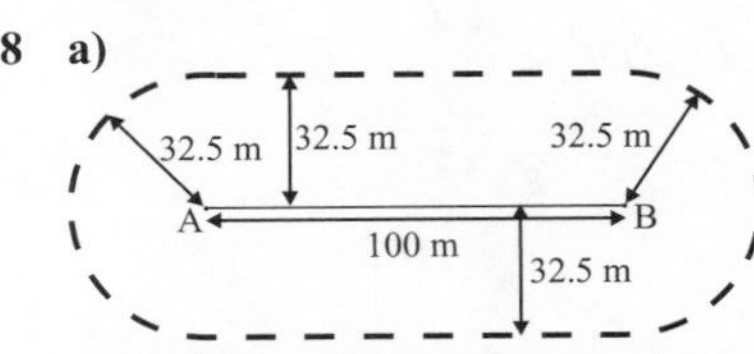

b) Distance around dashed path = (2 × 100) + (π × 65) = 404.2 m

Answers: P.89 — P.93

Q9

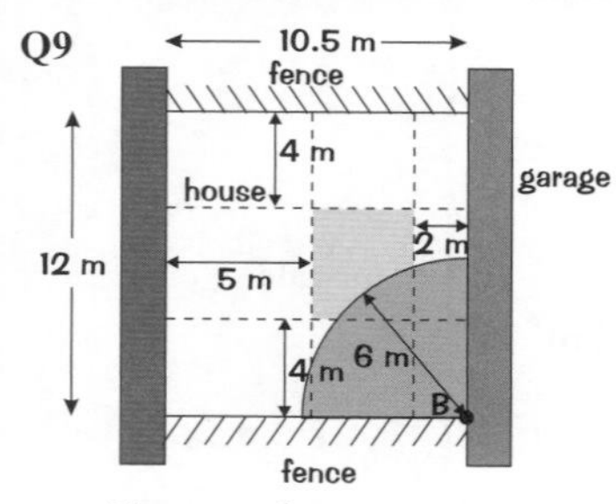

Not to scale

Q10 a)

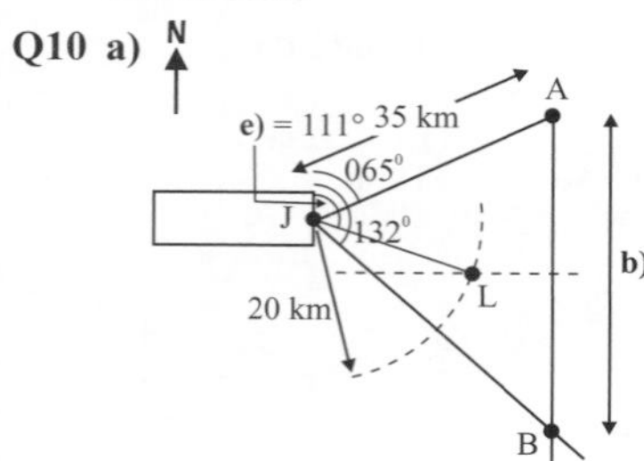

b) Length = 8.6 cm equivalent to 43 km.

c) 35 km in 2.5 hrs, so speed $= \frac{35}{2.5} = 14$ km/h.

d) and **e)** see diagram

Bearings P.90

Q1 **a)** 245°
b) 310°
c) 035°
d) 131°
e) 297°, 028°, 208°

Q2 **a)**

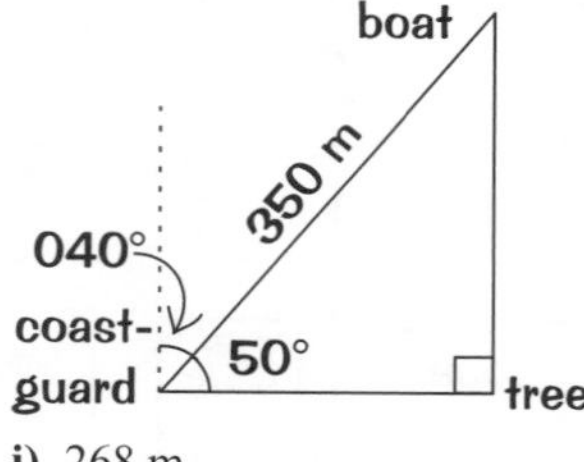

i) 268 m
ii) 225 m

b) $350^2 = 122\ 500$.
$225^2 + 268^2 = 122\ 449$

Q3

N
Z 129°
123 km
W
90 km
X 175°
165 km
Y

a) 96 km
b) 255 km

c) 266 km
d) 156°
e) 082°
f) 177°

Q4

start 165°
1200 m
210°
1500 m
finish

2500 m, 010°

Section Five — Pythagoras and Trigonometry

Pythagoras' Theorem P.91-P.93

Q1 **a)** 10.8 cm
b) 6.10 m
c) 5 cm
d) 27.0 mm
e) 8.49 m
f) 7.89 m
g) 9.60 cm
h) 4.97 cm
i) 6.80 cm
j) 8.5 cm

Q2 a = 3.32 cm
b = 6 cm
c = 6.26 m
d = 5.6 mm
e = 7.08 mm
f = 8.62 m
g = 6.42 m
h = 19.2 mm
i = 9.65 m
j = 48.7 mm

Q3 k = 6.55 cm
l = 4.87 m
m = 6.01 m
n = 12.4 cm
p = 5.22 cm
q = 7.07 cm
r = 7.50 m
s = 9.45 mm
t = 4.33 cm
u = 7.14 m

Q4 9.7 m

Q5 **a)** 12 cm, 7.94 cm
b) 40.9 cm
c) 89.7 cm²

Q6 314 m

Q7 91.9 cm

Q8 5.0 m

Q9 4.58 m

Q10
AB: 5 (don't need Pythagoras)
CD: $\sqrt{10} = 3.16$
EF: $\sqrt{13} = 3.61$
GH: $\sqrt{8} = 2.83$
JK: $\sqrt{5} = 2.24$
LM: $\sqrt{26} = 5.10$
PQ: $\sqrt{20} = 4.47$
RS: $\sqrt{45} = 6.71$
TU: $\sqrt{13} = 3.61$

Q11 **a)** 5
b) $\sqrt{17} = 4.12$
c) 5
d) $\sqrt{58} = 7.62$
e) $\sqrt{26} = 5.10$
f) parallelogram

Q12 **a)** $\sqrt{41} = 6.40$
b) $\sqrt{98} = 9.90$
c) $\sqrt{53} = 7.28$
d) $\sqrt{34} = 5.83$
e) 4 (don't need Pythagoras here)
f) $\sqrt{37} = 6.08$

Q13 **a)** $\sqrt{10} = 3.16$
b) $\sqrt{130} = 11.40$
c) $\sqrt{8} = 2.83$
d) $\sqrt{233} = 15.26$
e) $\sqrt{353} = 18.79$
f) $\sqrt{100} = 10$

Q14 192 km

Q15

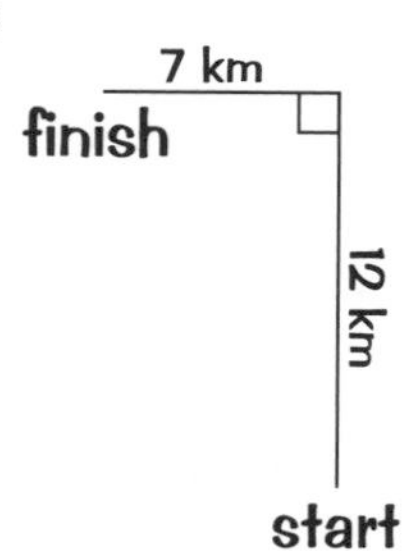

13.9 km from the starting point.
150° to return to base.

Answers: P.94 — P.97

Trigonometry — Sin, Cos, Tan P.94-P.96

		(tan)	(sin)	(cos)
Q1	a)	0.306	0.292	0.956
	b)	8.14	0.993	0.122
	c)	0.0875	0.0872	0.996
	d)	0.532	0.469	0.883
	e)	1	0.707	0.707

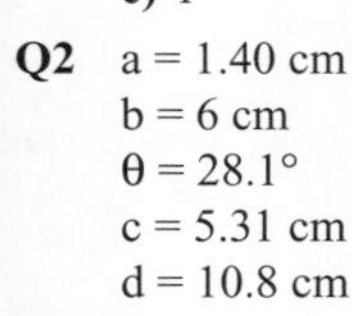

Q2 a = 1.40 cm
b = 6 cm
θ = 28.1°
c = 5.31 cm
d = 10.8 cm

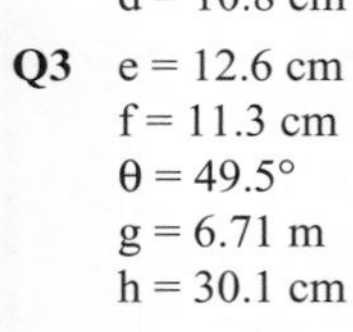

Q3 e = 12.6 cm
f = 11.3 cm
θ = 49.5°
g = 6.71 m
h = 30.1 cm

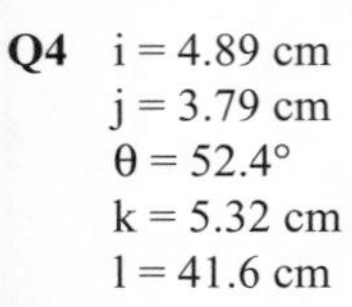

Q4 i = 4.89 cm
j = 3.79 cm
θ = 52.4°
k = 5.32 cm
l = 41.6 cm

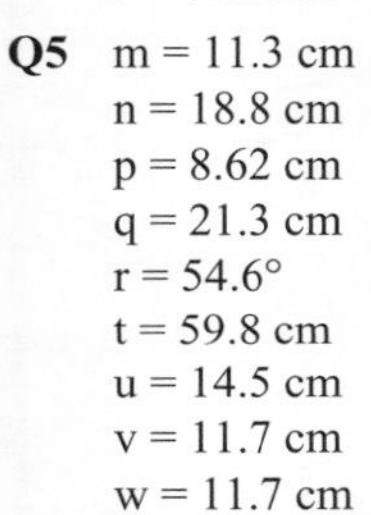

Q5 m = 11.3 cm
n = 18.8 cm
p = 8.62 cm
q = 21.3 cm
r = 54.6°
t = 59.8 cm
u = 14.5 cm
v = 11.7 cm
w = 11.7 cm

Q6 a)

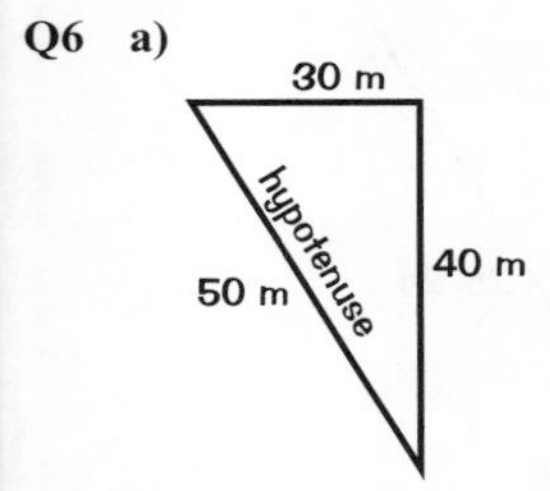

b) 36.9°

Q7 a)

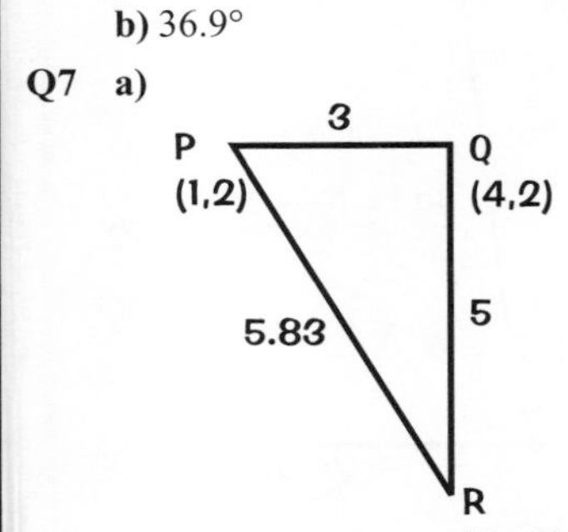

b) 59.0°
c) 31.0°

Q8 a)

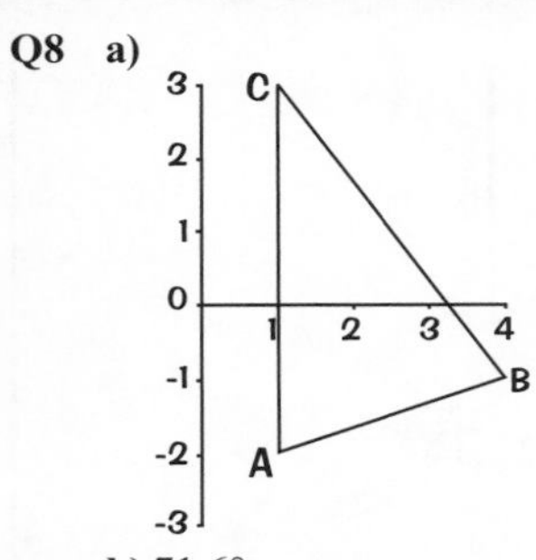

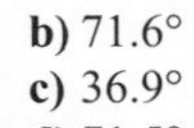

b) 71.6°
c) 36.9°
d) 71.5°

Q9 2.1 m

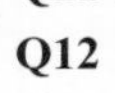

Q10 62°

Q11 20.5°

Q12

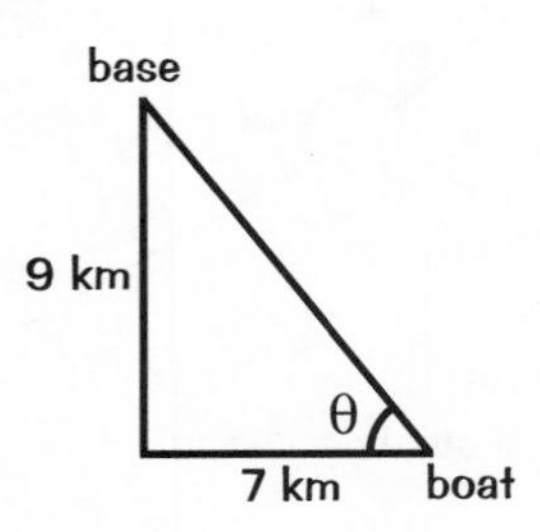

θ = 52.1°, bearing = 322°

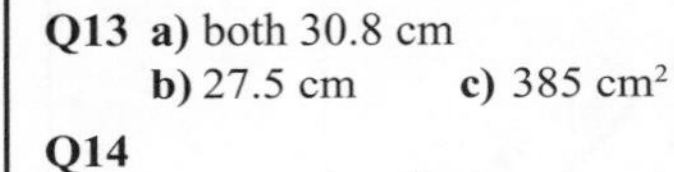

Q13 a) both 30.8 cm
b) 27.5 cm c) 385 cm²

Q14

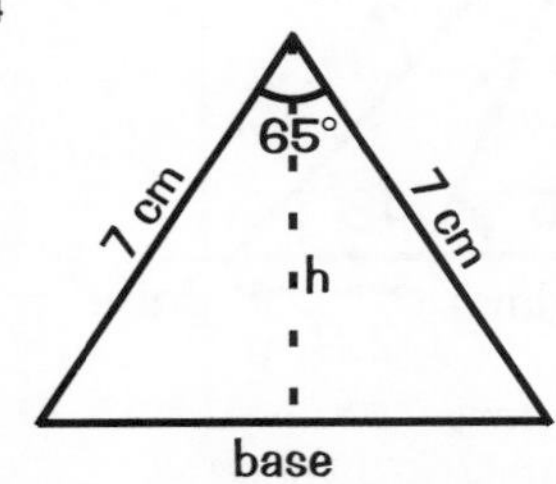

height = 5.90, base = 7.52, so area = 22.2 cm².

Q15 a) 8.23 cm
b) 4.75 cm c) 39.1 cm²

Q16 a) 10.8 cm
b) 150.8 cm² c) 21.0°

Q17

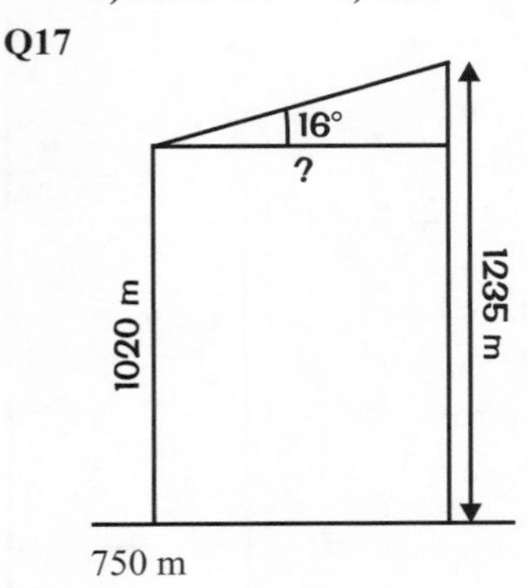

750 m

Q18

45 m
h
33°
1.3 m

25.8 m

Q19

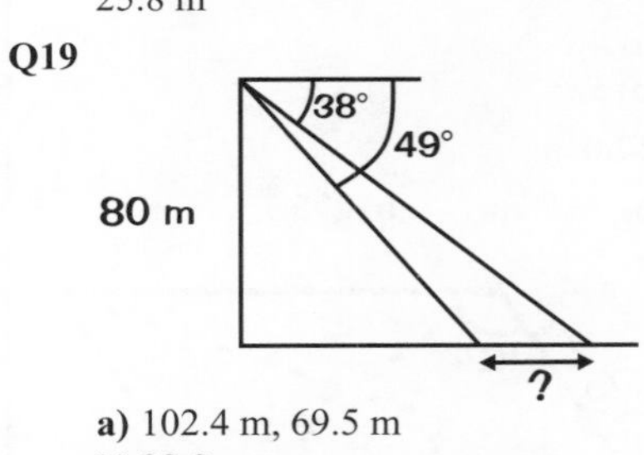

a) 102.4 m, 69.5 m
b) 32.9 m

Q20

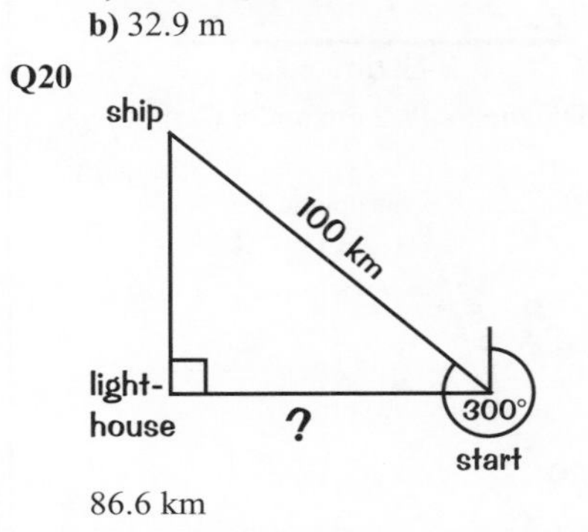

86.6 km

The Sine and Cosine Rules P.97-P.98

Q1 $a = 4.80$ cm
$b = 25.8$ mm
$c = 13.0$ cm
$d = 8.89$ m
$e = 18.4$ cm
$f = 5.26$ cm
$g = 9.96$ cm
$h = 20.2$ mm
$i = 3.72$ m
$j = 8.29$ cm

Q2 $k = 51°$
$l = 46°$
$m = 43°$
$p = 45°$
$q = 36°$
$r = 64°$
$s = 18°$
$t = 49°$
$u = 88°$

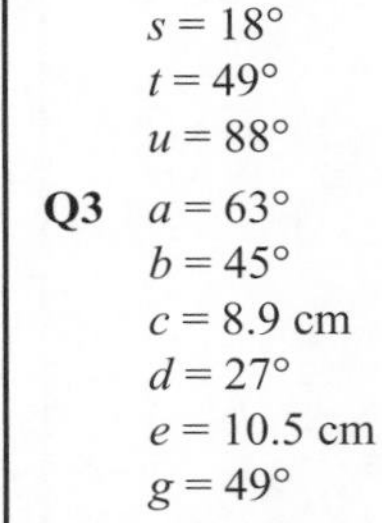

Q3 $a = 63°$
$b = 45°$
$c = 8.9$ cm
$d = 27°$
$e = 10.5$ cm
$g = 49°$

Answers: P.97 — P.100

$h = 78°$
$i = 5.0$ mm
$j = 68°$
$k = 203$ mm
$l = 127$ mm
$m = 24.1$ cm
$n = 149°$
$p = 16°$

Q4 **a)** 46°
b) 52° **c)** 82°

Q5 12.0 m

Q6 **a)** 28.8 km **b)** 295.5°

Q7

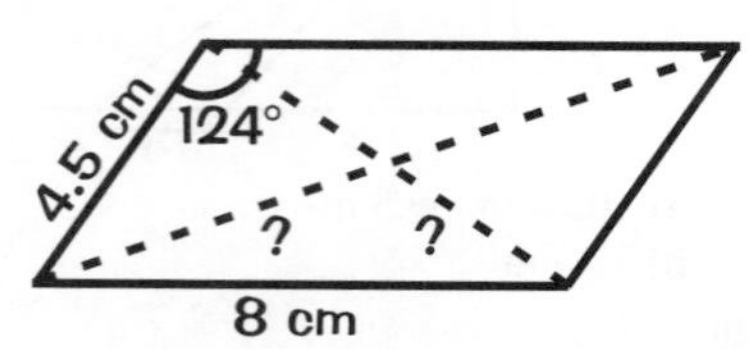

Diagonals 11.2 cm and 6.6 cm.

Q8

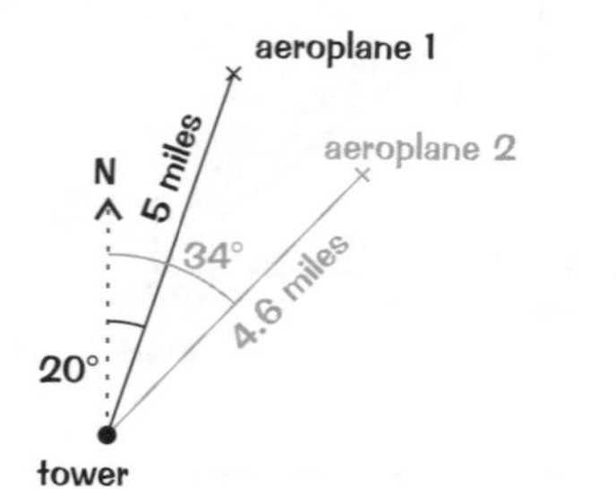

Distance = 1.2 miles.
The alarm should be ringing because the planes are less than 3 miles apart, so the software seems reliable.

Q9 **a)** 16.9 m
b) 12.4 m
c) 25.8 m
d) 19.5 m

Q10

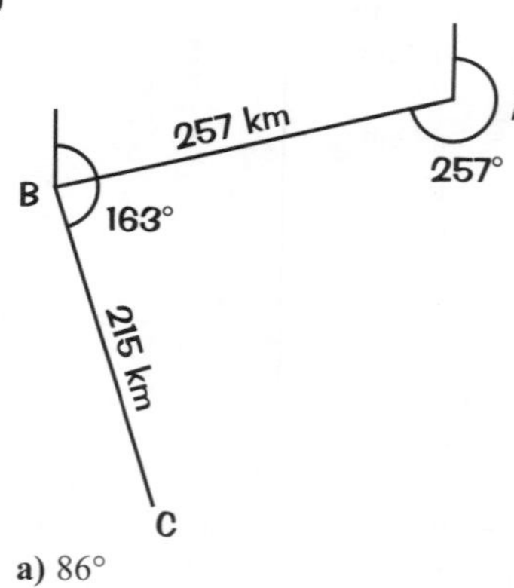

a) 86°
b) 323 km
c) 215°

Q11 **a)**

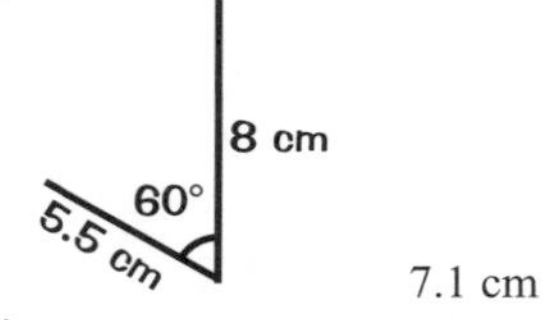

7.1 cm

b)

7 cm 118.5° 8 cm

14.5 cm
(118.5° comes from the fact that the minute hand is at 19.75 mins. 19.75 ÷ 60 × 360 = 118.5.)

c)

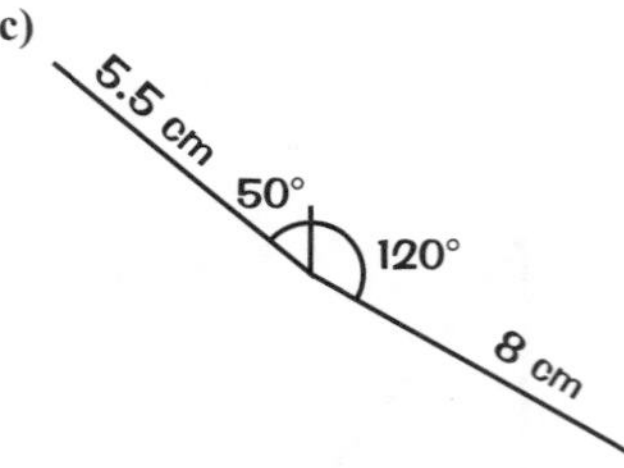

13.5 cm

Q12 Height of building = 35 m

Q13

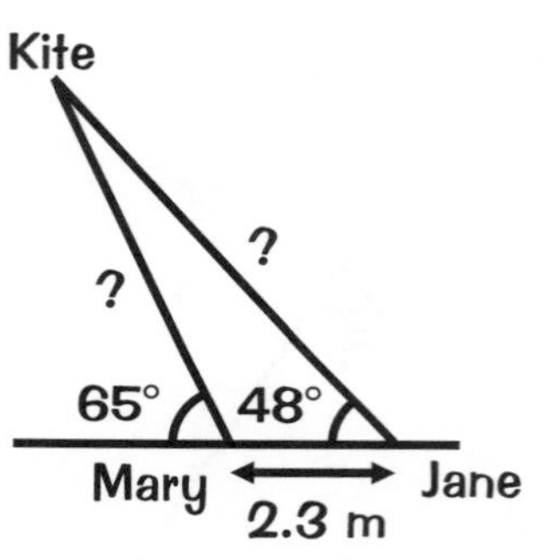

Mary's string = 5.85 m
Jane's string = 7.13 m

3D Pythagoras and Trigonometry P.99

Q1 **a)** 59.0°
b) 23.3 cm
c) 25 cm
d) 21.1°

Q2 **a)** 42.5 cm
b) 50.9 cm

Q3 **a)** 36.1 cm, 21.5 cm, 31.0 cm
b) 36.9 cm

Q4 **a)** 15.4 cm
b) 20.4 cm

Q5 The 85p box

Q6 **a)** 3.82 cm
b) 45.8 cm^2
c) 137.5 cm^3

Vectors P.100

Q1 **a)**

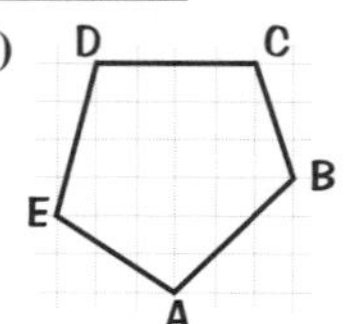

b) i) $\begin{pmatrix}-1\\-4\end{pmatrix}$
ii) $\begin{pmatrix}4\\0\end{pmatrix}$
iii) $\begin{pmatrix}5\\4\end{pmatrix}$
c) Isosceles

Q2 **a)** $\begin{pmatrix}2\\1\end{pmatrix}$ $\underset{\sim}{p}+\underset{\sim}{q}$

b) $\begin{pmatrix}2\\5\end{pmatrix}$ $\underset{\sim}{p}-\underset{\sim}{q}$

c) $\begin{pmatrix}6\\-2\end{pmatrix}$ $2\underset{\sim}{r}$

d) $\begin{pmatrix}1\\1\end{pmatrix}$ $\underset{\sim}{s}+\underset{\sim}{p}$

e) $\begin{pmatrix}6\\10\end{pmatrix}$ $2\underset{\sim}{p}-2\underset{\sim}{s}$

f) $\begin{pmatrix}-1\\-8\end{pmatrix}$ $3\underset{\sim}{q}+\underset{\sim}{s}$

g) $\begin{pmatrix}6\\0\end{pmatrix}$ $2\underset{\sim}{r}-\underset{\sim}{q}$

h) $\begin{pmatrix}6\\-3\end{pmatrix}$ $\tfrac{1}{2}\underset{\sim}{q}+2\underset{\sim}{r}$

i) $\begin{pmatrix}0\\-1\end{pmatrix}$ $\underset{\sim}{p}+2\underset{\sim}{s}$

Answers: P.100 — P.104

j) $\begin{pmatrix}-6\\0\end{pmatrix}$

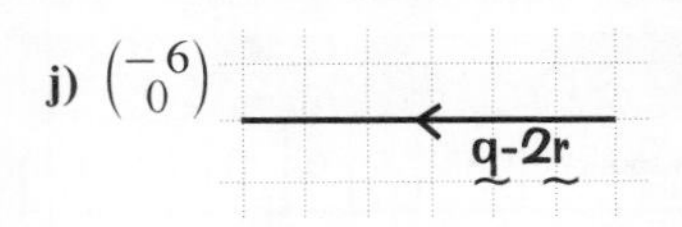

Q3 **a)** $2\underset{\sim}{y}$ **d)** $2\underset{\sim}{y} + 2\underset{\sim}{x}$

b) $\underset{\sim}{y} + \underset{\sim}{x}$ **e)** $4\underset{\sim}{y} + 2\underset{\sim}{x}$

c) $-\underset{\sim}{y} - \underset{\sim}{x}$ **f)** $2\underset{\sim}{x}$

Q4 **a) i)** $\overrightarrow{ED}$ or $\overrightarrow{AF}$ **v)** $\overrightarrow{BE}$

ii) $\overrightarrow{EF}$ or $\overrightarrow{DC}$ **vi)** $\overrightarrow{AC}$

iii) $\overrightarrow{AE}$ **vii)** $\overrightarrow{EC}$ or $\overrightarrow{AB}$

iv) $\overrightarrow{BA}$ **viii)** $\overrightarrow{EB}$

b) i) 48 cm^2 **ii)** 60 cm^2

Section Six — Statistics and Probability

Sampling Methods and Bias P.101-P.103

Q1 A population is a group of things you're interested in investigating.

Q2 **a)** All 20- to 30-year-old women
b) All the public parks in London
c) All the squirrels in Britain
d) All football players in the Premier League

Q3 **a)** All the lakes and ponds in Nottingham
b) Either a list of all the lakes and ponds in Nottingham or a map showing all lakes and ponds in Nottingham.

Q4 **a)** All the moorland dung beetles in the UK
b) Because it would be extremely difficult and impractical for him to be sure that he had surveyed every single moorland dung beetle in the UK.

Q5 E.g. Reason 1 — The average wage of three people who are the same age might not be representative of the whole population — e.g. a 13-year-old will probably earn less than a 19-year-old.
Reason 2 — the sample is too small, so it won't be representative of the whole population.

Q6 **a)** All the supporters of Whitby F.C.
b) E.g. Not everyone on the electoral register will support Whitby F.C. / Some supporters may not be on Whitby's electoral register (e.g. because they're too young or live elsewhere).

Q7 Choosing something at random means every item in the population has an equal chance of being chosen.

Q8 A computer and calculator.

Q9 **a)** The sample is not random and so might not be representative of all the cakes.
b) Number all the cakes from 1 to 50, reading across each row. Generate 5 random numbers (e.g. using a calculator, computer program or by picking numbers out of a bag) between 1 and 50. Select the 5 cake weights that correspond to the 5 numbers you have generated.

Q10 **a)** Total number of staff = 1000. So, rounding to the nearest person, the sample would include:
$(99/1000) \times 100 = 9.9$
— 10 receptionists,
$(53/1000) \times 100 = 5.3$
— 5 salon managers,
$(251/1000) \times 100 = 25.1$
— 25 colour technicians
$(597/1000) \times 100 = 59.7$
— 60 stylists.
b) A stratified sample is likely to be more representative of the different employee types within the company.

Q11 **a)** So that each year group's representation in the sample is proportional to the size of the year group.
b) Total number of students = 1600.
$(398 \div 1600) \times 40 = 9.95$
Rounded to the nearest person, there would be 10 Year 7 students in the sample.
c) The proportion of Year 11 students is 199/1600, which is roughly 1/8. As we know there are 10 Year 11's in the sample, the group must be 80 pupils.

Q12 **a)** Reason 1 – They have only sampled from one sixth-form college, and excluded all the other sixth-forms in the UK.
Reason 2 – Not all students at the college will be doing chemistry, so the results won't fairly represent the population of chemistry students.
b) They should have sampled from all sixth-form chemistry students in the UK.

Q13 **a)** This excludes any residents who don't shop in Cheapeez or who don't go shopping early on Saturday mornings.
b) They should have sampled from all the residents of Devon.

Q14 **a)** E.g. The sample is biased because it excludes people not shopping on the high street/Saturday morning. The proportions of the different age groups in the sample are different to the proportions in the whole of Yeovil, so it doesn't fairly represent the population of Yeovil.
b) The council should have sampled from all the residents of Yeovil.

Q15 **a)** Fred's sample is non-random – the people in it are likely to be commuters. So, it doesn't fairly represent the whole population.
b) Fred should use a simple random sample – e.g. a random sample chosen from all public transport users in his town.

Q16 **a)** People in a newsagents are likely to be there to buy a newspaper.
b) At that time on a Sunday, people who go to church are likely to be at church.
c) The bridge club is unlikely to be representative of the population as a whole.

Collecting Data P.104-P.105

Q1 **a)** Quantitative data is data that can be measured with numbers.
b) Qualitative data

Q2 **a)** Qualitative
b) Quantitative
c) Quantitative
d) Qualitative

Q3 **a)** Discrete
b) Any discrete data set, e.g. number of pupils in a class.
c) Continuous data is data that can take any value in a range.
d) Any continuous data set, e.g. times, heights, weights, etc.

Q4 **a)** Discrete
b) Continuous
c) Discrete
d) Continuous

Q5 E.g.

Length of time (mins)	1-10	11-20	21-30	31-40	41-50
Number of people	5	10	5	5	5

Answers: P.105 — P.112

Q6 a) There is no time period specified / the question is subjective – "very often" can mean different things to different people.
b) Any sensible answer with tick boxes, e.g. "How many times a week do you visit the school canteen? Never, 1-2 times, 3-4 times or more than 4 times."

Q7 This question is not relevant to what the council wants to find out.

Q8 a) The question is ambiguous because the age classes overlap, e.g. someone who's 30 could go in either the 18-30 or 30-40 group.
b) Change the answers to:
"i) Under 18
ii) 18 to 30
iii) 31 to 40
iv) 41 to 60
v) over 60".

Q9 The question is leading because it suggests an answer. This means it is not a fair question — people might be more likely to say 'yes'.

Q10 a) E.g.

Café Questionnaire

1) Please tick the box to show how often you visit the café:
daily ☐ weekly ☐ fortnightly ☐
monthly ☐ less than monthly ☐

2) Please tick the box to show how often you buy cola:
daily ☐ weekly ☐ fortnightly ☐
monthly ☐ less than monthly ☐

b) She will miss out the people who just buy drinks from the hot and cold drinks machines.

Mean, Median, Mode and Range P.106-P.107

Q1 3 tries

Q2 mean = 1.333 (to 3 dp)
median = 1.5
mode = 2
range = 11

Q3 a) mean = £12,944, or £13,000 to the nearest £500
median = £12,000
mode = £7,500
b) mode
c) E.g. mean — the high value will attract people to the job, but it is also a good indication of their employees' average commission (i.e. it won't mislead people).

Q4 a) 0 minutes
b) 0 minutes
c) 0 minutes
d) No, according to the raw data.

Q5 73.5 kg

Q6 20 kg

Q7 97%

Q8 a) 22 **b)** 74

Q9 a) 3.5
b) 3.5 **c)** 5

Q10 a) Both spend a mean of 2 hours.
b) The range for Jim is 3 hours and for Bob is 2 hours.
c) The amount of TV that Jim watches each night is more variable than the amount that Bob watches.

Q11 a) 1 day
b) 2 days
c) The statement is true according to the data.

Averages and Spread P.108-109

Q1 a) 65 g
b) The 2nd quartile (or Q_2)

Q2 a) 1020 – 80 = 940
b) 510
c) 700
d) 840

Q3 200

Q4 a) 325 **b)** 50

Q5

Stem	Leaves
0	7 8
1	1 3 5 8
2	1 2 3 6 9
3	1 3 7 9
4	1 8
5	0

Q6 a) 90 years
b) 120 years
c) 70 years

Q7 Mean (A) = 3·61 fillings per child
Mean (B) = 2·08 fillings per child
Mode (A) = 4 fillings per child
Mode (B) = 2 fillings per child
Median (A) = 4 fillings per child
Median (B) = 2 fillings per child
(all other things being equal, I would say that the dental hygienist has made a difference to the number of fillings received by each child.)

Frequency Tables — Finding Averages P.110-P.111

Q1 a) 12 **b)** 12
c) 2

Q2 a)

Subject	M	E	F	A	S
Frequency	5	7	3	4	6

b) 36 French lessons **c)** English

Q3

Length (m)	4 and under	6	8	10	12	14 and over
Frequency	3	5	6	4	1	1

a) 8 m **b)** 8 m **c)** 14 m

Q4

Weight (kg)	Frequency	Weight × Frequency
51	40	2040
52	30	1560
53	45	2385
54	10	540
55	5	275

a) 52 kg
b) 2 kg
c) 53 kg
d) 52 kg (to nearest kg)

Q5 mean = 3.75
mode = 3
median = 4

Q6 a) 4
b) 3 **c)** 3.2 (to 1 dp)

Q7 a) i) False, mode is 8.
ii) False, they are equal.
iii) True
b) iv)

Grouped Frequency Tables P.112

Q1 a)

Speed (km/h)	$40 \leq s < 45$	$45 \leq s < 50$	$50 \leq s < 55$	$55 \leq s < 60$	$60 \leq s < 65$
Frequency	4	8	10	7	3
Mid-Interval	42.5	47.5	52.5	57.5	62.5
Frequency × Mid-Interval	170	380	525	402.5	187.5

Estimated mean = 52 km/h (to nearest km/h)
b) 22 skiers **c)** 20 skiers

Q2 a)

Weight (kg)	Tally	Frequency	Mid-Interval	Frequency × Mid-Interval
$200 \leq w < 250$	IIII	4	225	900
$250 \leq w < 300$	卌	5	275	1375
$300 \leq w < 350$	卌 II	7	325	2275
$350 \leq w < 400$	II	2	375	750

b) 294 kg (to nearest kg)
c) $300 \leqslant w < 350$ kg

Q3 a)

Number	$0 \leq n < 0.2$	$0.2 \leq n < 0.4$	$0.4 \leq n < 0.6$	$0.6 \leq n < 0.8$	$0.8 \leq n < 1$
Tally	卌 卌 II	卌 I	卌 卌 II	卌 卌	卌 III
Frequency	12	6	12	10	8
Mid-Interval	0.1	0.3	0.5	0.7	0.9
Frequency × Mid-Interval	1.2	1.8	6	7	7.2

b) $0 \leqslant n < 0.2$ and $0.4 \leqslant n < 0.6$
c) $0.4 \leqslant n < 0.6$
d) 0.483 (3 dp)

Answers: P.113 — P.115

Cumulative Frequency P.113-P.114

Q1 accept:
a) 133-134 **c)** 136-137
b) 127-128 **d)** 8-10

Q2 a)

Number of passengers	0≤n<50	50≤n<100	100≤n<150	150≤n<200	200≤n<250	250≤n<300
Frequency	2	7	10	5	3	1
Cumulative Frequency	2	9	19	24	27	28
Mid-Interval	25	75	125	175	225	275
Frequency × Mid-Interval	50	525	1250	875	675	275

Estimated mean = 130 passengers (to nearest whole number)

b)

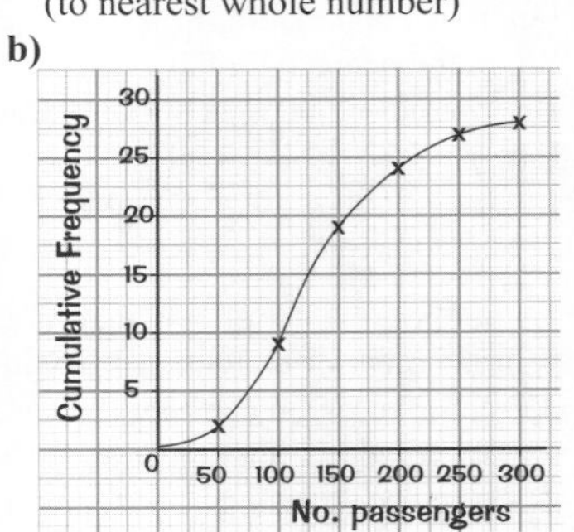

accept median of 118-122 passengers

c) 100 ≤ n < 150

Q3 a)

Mark (%)	0≤m<20	20≤m<40	40≤m<60	60≤m<80	80≤m<100
Frequency	2	12	18	5	3
Cumulative Frequency	2	14	32	37	40

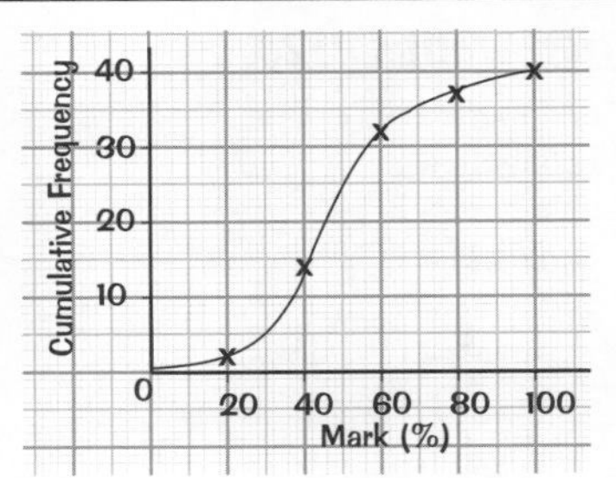

b) 36%-38%
c) 19%-21%
d) 45%-47%

Q4

Score	31≤s<41	41≤s<51	51≤s<61	61≤s<71	71≤s<81	81≤s<91	91≤s<101
Frequency	4	12	21	32	19	8	4
Cumulative frequency	4	16	37	69	88	96	100

a) 61 ≤ s < 71
b) 61 ≤ s < 71

c)

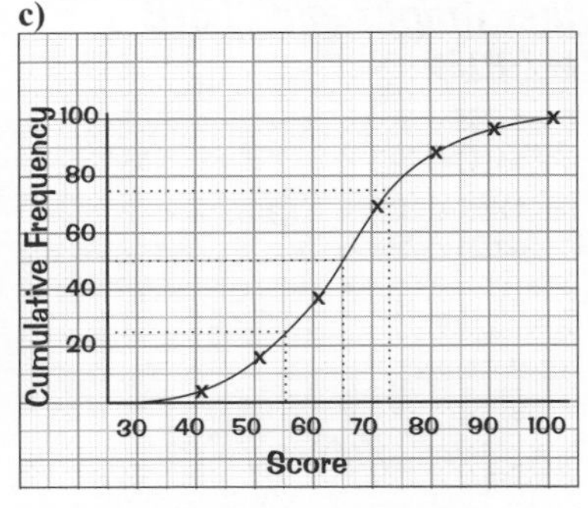

median = 65 (accept 64-66)
d) 73 – 55 = 18 (accept 17-19)

Q5 a)

Life (hours)	Frequency	Cumulative Frequency
900 ≤ L < 1000	10	10
1000 ≤ L < 1100	12	22
1100 ≤ L < 1200	15	37
1200 ≤ L < 1300	18	55
1300 ≤ L < 1400	22	77
1400 ≤ L < 1500	17	94
1500 ≤ L < 1600	14	108
1600 ≤ L < 1700	9	117

b) 1300 ≤ L < 1400
c)

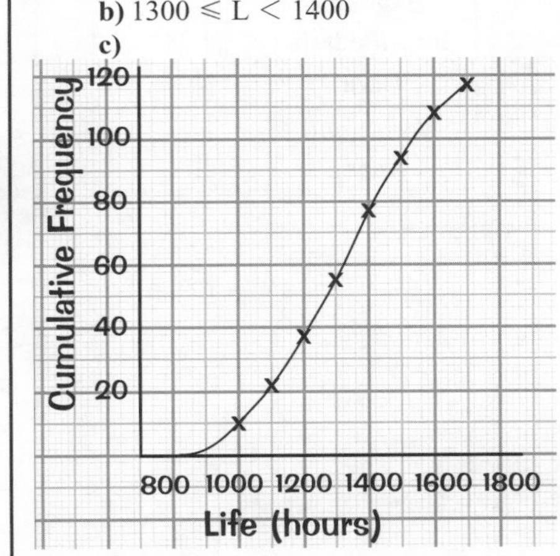

median = 1320 hours (±20)
d) lower quartile = 1150 (±20)
upper quartile = 1460 (±20)

Q6 a)

Time	2:00≤s<2:30	2:30≤s<3:00	3:00≤s<3:30	3:30≤s<4:00	4:00≤s<4:30
Tally	1	卌	卌卌1111	卌11	111
Frequency	1	5	14	7	3
Cumulative Frequency	1	6	20	27	30

b)

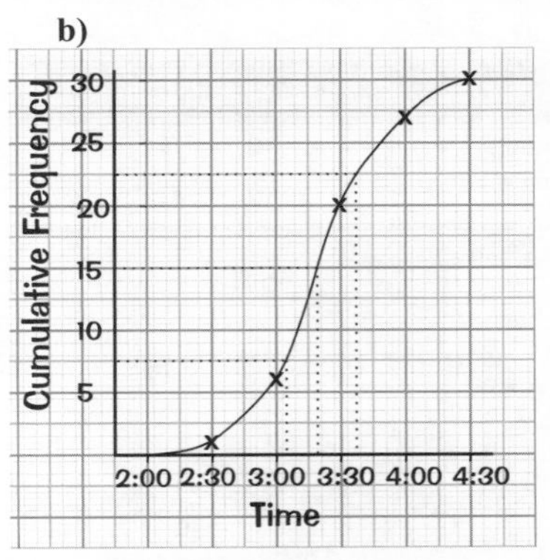

c) median = 3:19 (±3)
upper quartile = 3:37 (±3)
lower quartile = 3:05 (±3)
d) 0:32 (±5)

Histograms and Frequency Density P.115-P.116

Q1 4 × 10 = 40 people

Q2

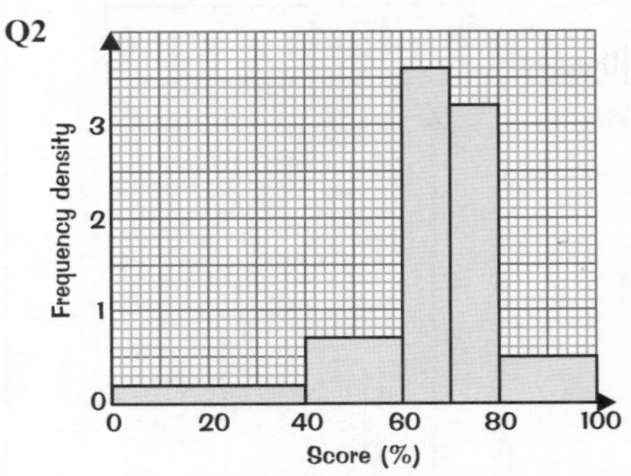

Q3 a) Frequency for $150 < x \leqslant 200$ = 275

b)

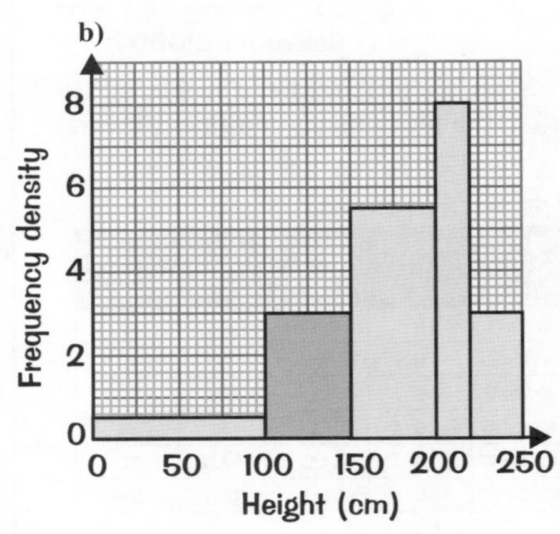

Answers: P.116 — P.120

Q4 a)

Weight (kg)	0≤w<2	2≤w<4	4≤w<7	7≤w<9	9≤w<15
Frequency	3	2	6	9	12
Frequency density	1.5	1	2	4.5	2

b)

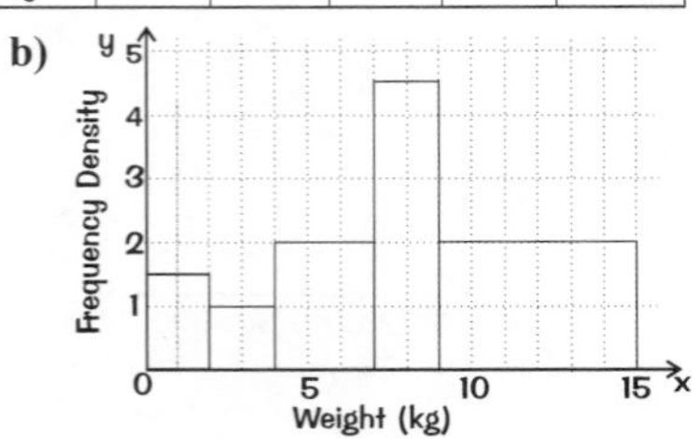

c) 23 hives

Q5 a)

Salary (£1000s)	0 ≤ s < 10	10 ≤ s < 20	20 ≤ s < 30	30 ≤ s < 40	40 ≤ s < 50
Frequency	10	25	42	20	3
Frequency Density	1	2.5	4.2	2	0.3

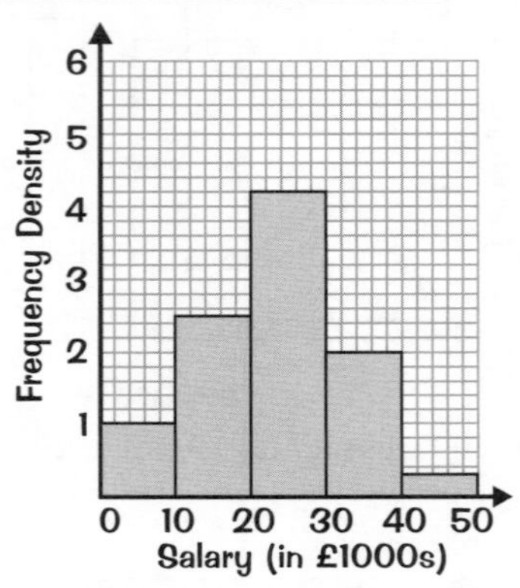

b) E.g. there are more people with higher salaries now than 10 years ago.

Q6 a)

Milk (litres)	Frequency	Frequency density	Mid-interval	Frequency × mid-interval
0≤C<1	6	6	0.5	3
1≤C<5	6	1.5	3	18
5≤C<8	6	2	6.5	39
8≤C<10	6	3	9	54
10≤C<15	6	1.2	12.5	75
15≤C<20	6	1.2	17.5	105

b) 8.2 litres (to 1 d.p.)

c)

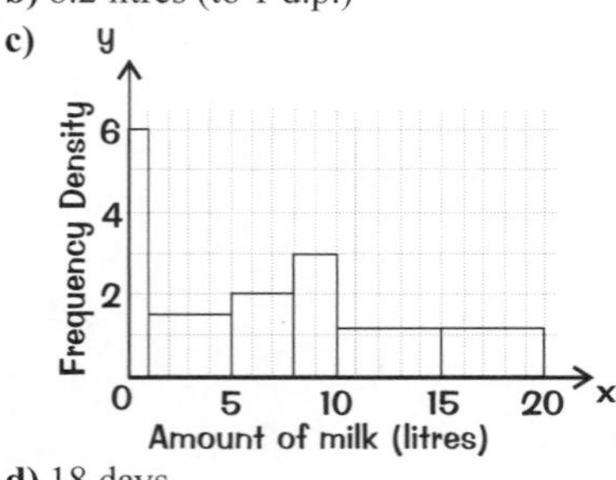

d) 18 days

Other Graphs and Charts P.117-P.119

Q1 **a)** 35
b) 52
c) 9
d) 21

Q2 **a)**

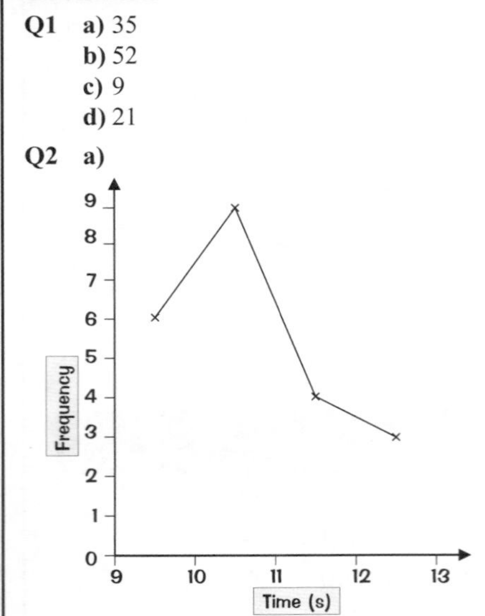

b) 22
c) 19

Q3 **a)** Tally chart

Level of skier	No.
Beginner	𝍸 |||
Intermediate	𝍸 𝍸
Good	||||
Very good	|||
Racer	|||

b) Bar chart

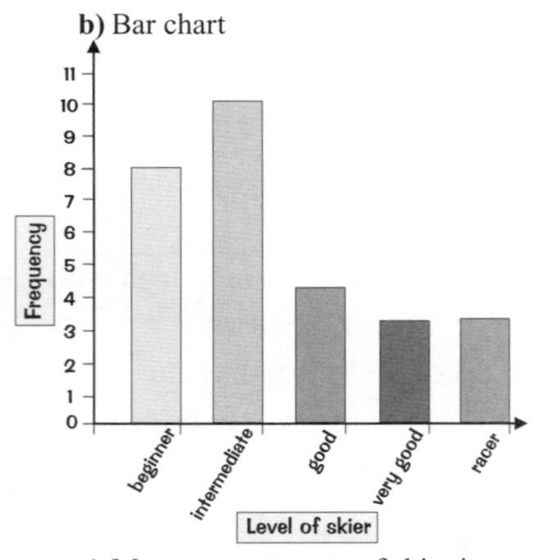

c) Most common type of skier is Intermediate.

Q4 Complaints have not "tailed off" - they have remained the same (approx 10,850) per month.
The number of complaints is not increasing but there are still 10,850 per month, every month.
The products cannot possibly be getting made to a higher quality if the complaints remain the same each month.

Q5 $\frac{360°}{100} = 3.6°$ per gram

Carbohydrate	3.6 × 35 = 126°
Protein	3.6 × 15 = 54°
Fat	3.6 × 10 = 36°
Magical Fairy Dust	3.6 × 40 = 144°
	360°

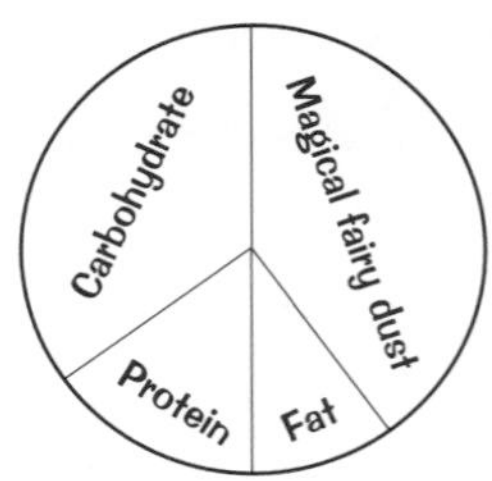

Q6 Sherrington 380,000 = 146°
(approx) 2600 visitors = 1°
So, to the nearest 10,000:
Brompton = 2600 × 118° ≈ 310,000
Barny = 2600 × 44° ≈ 110,000
Livsea = 2600 × 50° ≈ 130,000

Q7 **c)**

Q8 It's not possible to tell whether more people voted for the Green Party in 2009, because you can't tell how many people voted in either election.

Q9 **a)** Monday, Wednesday and Thursday.
b) Monday

Q10 **a)** About 60%
b) About 50%
c) On average, women live longer than men / husbands are usually older than wives. So, women in their 90s are far more likely to have lost their husbands than men in their 90s are to have lost their wives.

Scatter Graphs P.120

Q1 A: labelled S
B: labelled R
C: labelled P
D: labelled U

Q2 **a)**

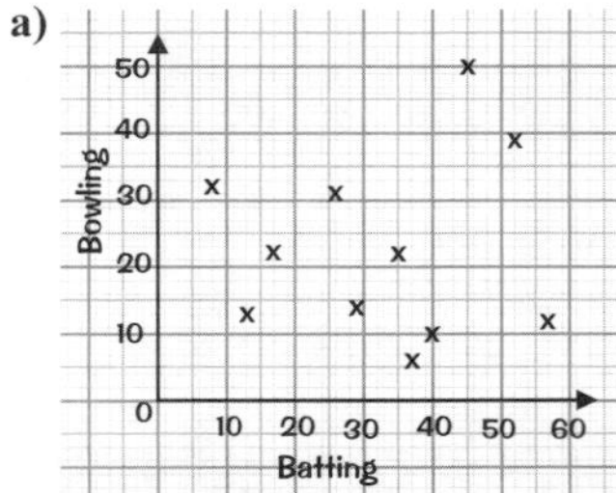

b) There is no correlation.
c) No — if he were correct the graph would show negative correlation.

Answers: P.120 — P.124

Q3 a), b)

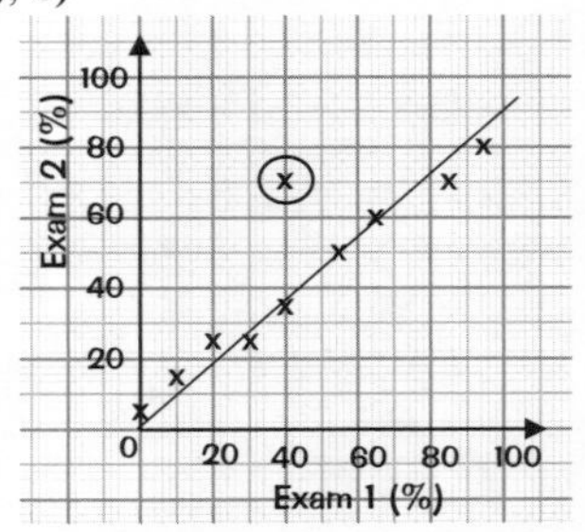

c) 46% (accept any answer between 40% and 50%)

Probability P.121-P.124

Q1 **a)** 1/2 **c)** 1/6
b) 2/3 **d)** 0

And so should be arranged approximately like this on the number line.

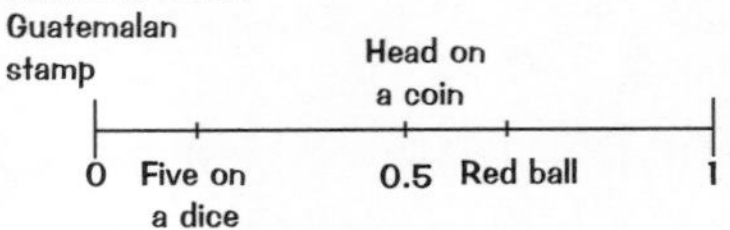

Q2 Debbie's chance of winning would be 1/9. This is greater than 0.1, so she would choose to play.

Q3 The probability of a head is still 1/2

Q4 1 – 0.27 = 0.73 or 73/100

Q5 **a)** 5/12 **c)** 3/12 = 1/4
b) 4/12 = 1/3 **d)** 9/12 = 3/4

Q6 **a)** 40/132 = 10/33
b) P(car being blue or green) = 45/132
P(not blue or green) = 87/132 = 29/44

Q7

	1	2	3	4	5
1	1,1	1,2	1,3	1,4	1,5
2	2,1	2,2	2,3	2,4	2,5
3	3,1	3,2	3,3	3,4	3,5
4	4,1	4,2	4,3	4,4	4,5
5	5,1	5,2	5,3	5,4	5,5
6	6,1	6,2	6,3	6,4	6,5

Q8 **a)**

Outcome	Frequency
W	8
D	5
L	7

b) The 3 outcomes are not equally likely.
c) 1/4
d) They are most likely to win.

Q9 **a)** $\frac{1}{13}$
b) $\frac{2}{39}$ **c)** $\frac{1}{36}$

Q10 **a)** $\frac{7}{12}$ **b)** $\frac{7}{12}$
c) The two events can both happen at the same time, since 3 is a white.

Q11 **a)** $\frac{2}{5}$
b) $\frac{4}{15}$ **c)** $\frac{2}{3}$

Q12 **a)** (1,1), (1,2), (1,3), (1,4), (1,5), (1,6), (1,7), (2,1), (2,2), (2,3), (2,4), (2,5), (2,6), (2,7), (3,1), (3,2), (3,3), (3,4), (3,5), (3,6), (3,7)

b)

	1	2	3	4	5	6	7
1	2	3	4	5	6	7	8
2	3	4	5	6	7	8	9
3	4	5	6	7	8	9	10

c) $\frac{1}{7}$ **d)** $\frac{11}{21}$
e) $\frac{2}{7}$ **f)** $\frac{5}{7}$
g) Subtract the answer to part **e)** from 1.

Q13 **a)**

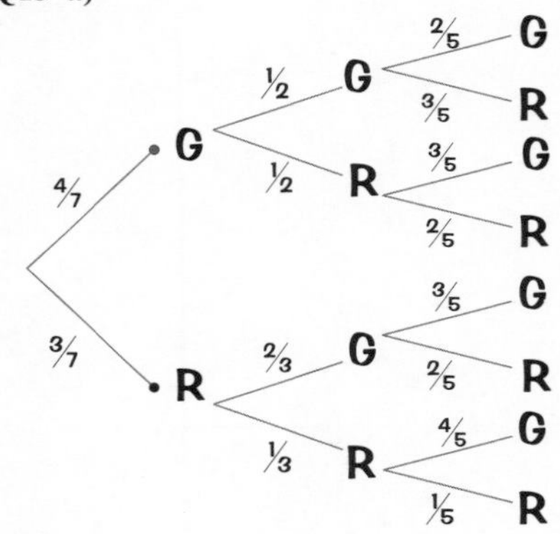

b) $\frac{18}{35}$
c) $\frac{3}{7}$

Q14 **a)** 14/40 or 0.35
b) 24/60 = 0.4
c) 38/100 = 0.38

Q15 4 times

Q16

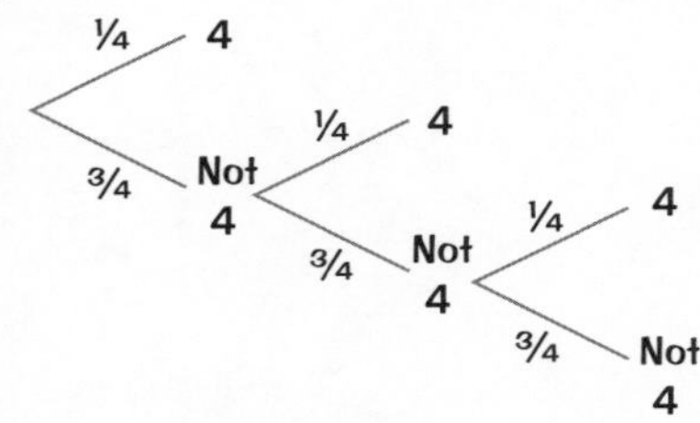

a) $\frac{3}{16}$
b) $\frac{37}{64}$

Q17 **a)**

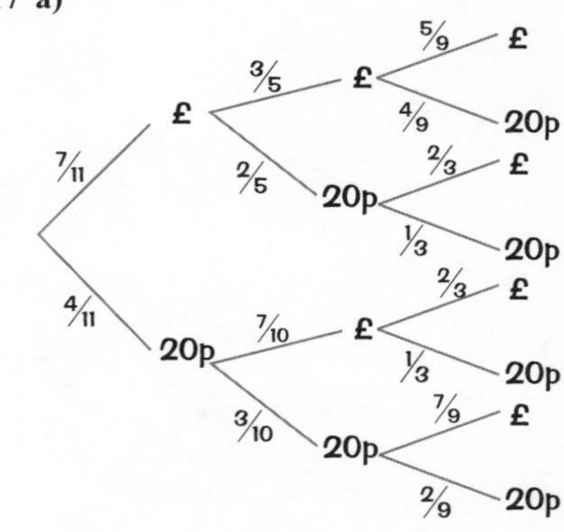

b) $\frac{28}{55}$ **c)** $\frac{46}{165}$

Q18 **a)** $\frac{1}{4}$
b) $\frac{1}{2}$ **c)** $\frac{1}{2}$

Q19 $\frac{1}{28}$

0913 - 11296

CGP

ISBN 978 1 84146 577 7

9 781841 465777

MQHA45